Master the SPaG basics with CGP!

This Foundation Question Book from CGP is perfect for helping pupils aged 9-10 get to grips with English in Year 5.

It's bursting with practice questions to help pupils improve the essential grammar, punctuation and spelling skills they'll need.

Each topic starts with helpful examples and there are answers to every question at the back of the book!

What CGP is all about

Our sole aim here at CGP is to produce the highest quality books
— carefully written, immaculately presented
and dangerously close to being funny.

Then we work our socks off to get them out to you
— at the cheapest possible prices.

Contents

Grammar

Punctuation

Contents

Spelling

Published by CGP

Editors
Heather Cowley, Zoe Fenwick, Melissa Gardner, Gabrielle Richardson,
Hannah Roscoe, Rebecca Russell, James Summersgill, Sean Walsh
With thanks to Tom Carney and Alison Griffin for the proofreading.
With thanks to Jan Greenway for the copyright research.
Thumb illustration used throughout the book © iStock.com.
The Grammar and Punctuation sections contain public sector information licensed under the Open Government Licence v3.0.
http://www.nationalarchives.gov.uk/doc/open-government-licence/version/3/

ISBN: 978 1 78908 335 4

Clipart from Corel®
Printed by Elanders Ltd, Newcastle upon Tyne.
Based on the classic CGP style created by Richard Parsons.

Text, design, layout and original illustrations © Coordination Group Publications Ltd. (CGP) 2019
All rights reserved.

Section 1 — Word Types

Nouns

Nouns are words that name things.

Concrete nouns are names for things that you can see, touch, smell or hear. ⟶ dog   bed   book

Abstract nouns are names for ideas or feelings. ⟶ trust   bravery   anger

Collective nouns are names for groups of people, animals or things.

a swarm of bees   a bunch of grapes

---

1 Draw lines to match each <u>noun</u> with the correct <u>label</u>.

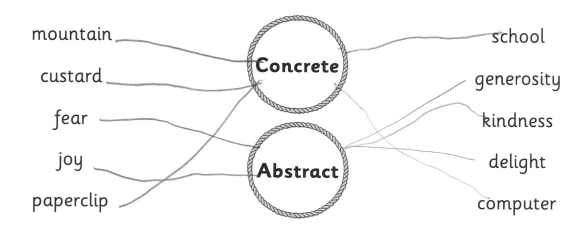

mountain

custard

fear

joy

paperclip

Concrete

Abstract

school

generosity

kindness

delight

computer

---

2 Tick the boxes next to the phrases that contain a <u>collective noun</u>.

a herd of cows ☑

my yellow raincoat ☐

the class of children ☑

this delicious pizza ☐

your new kitten ☐

a pack of wolves ☑

"I can identify different types of noun."

Adjectives

Adjectives are words that tell us more about a noun.

| the blue shirt | a fizzy drink | the beautiful view |

1 Show which words below are <u>adjectives</u> by drawing lines to the puzzle piece.

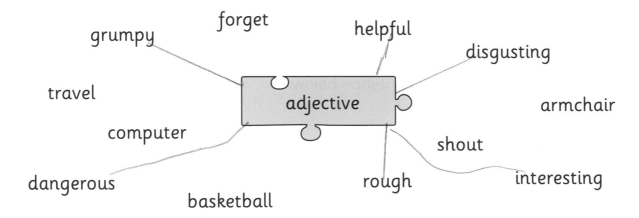

forget

grumpy

helpful

disgusting

travel

adjective

armchair

computer

shout

dangerous

rough

interesting

basketball

2 Circle the correct <u>adjective</u> to complete the sentences.

The gardener cut back the <u>nervous</u> / <u>spiky</u> rose bush.

Leon put his <u>filthy</u> / <u>rusty</u> football kit in the laundry basket.

3 Replace the underlined <u>adjectives</u> with more interesting <u>adjectives</u>.

The rides at the theme park were <u>good</u>. Overall, I had a <u>good</u> day.

amazing   great

I don't like aeroplanes — flying is <u>bad</u> and the food tastes <u>bad</u>.

horrible   gross

"I know what adjectives are and how to use them."

Section 1 — Word Types

Verbs

Verbs **are** doing or being **words.**

| Lola plays tennis. | You open the door. | I am hungry. |

Verbs **change** depending on who is doing the action.

| I walk to school. | She walks to school. |

---

1 Underline the <u>verb</u> in each sentence below.

Maya makes models out of clay.

The hamster always hides behind the sofa.

That book has a very happy ending.

My uncle is a policeman in London.

On Tuesdays, Jacob takes the bus home.

You are much taller than my brother.

Don't forget that verbs can be 'doing' or 'being' words.

---

2 Circle the <u>correct</u> form of each verb to finish these sentences.

Harry <u>rides</u> / <u>ride</u> his bike.

We <u>live</u> / <u>lives</u> in Bristol.

Evan <u>enjoy</u> / <u>enjoys</u> school.

You <u>read</u> / <u>reads</u> short stories.

My best friend <u>are</u> / <u>is</u> from Spain.

I <u>do</u> / <u>does</u> karate on Mondays.

They <u>cooks</u> / <u>cook</u> pizza.

Felix <u>have</u> / <u>has</u> three cats.

"I know what verbs are and how to use them."

Adverbs

Adverbs are words that describe verbs, adjectives and other adverbs.

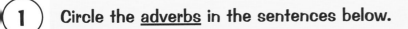

She easily won the race.

'easily' is the adverb.

The kitten is very fluffy.

He swims really slowly.

Adverbs often end with -ly.

1 Circle the <u>adverbs</u> in the sentences below.

My large, brown, bulky parcel finally arrived.

Remi and Tomas usually eat their lunch in the hall.

Mum says it is extremely difficult to become a lawyer.

The magician suddenly turned into a frog!

My brother plays a really nice guitar.

2 Add the correct <u>adverb</u> from the boxes to the sentences below.

| usually | very | perfectly | sternly | gently |

Only use each adverb once.

Rania .... took her hamster out of its cage.

We arrived at the airport .... early.

The police officer looked .... at the thief.

The gymnast performed his routine ....

Yusef doesn't have a watch, so he's .... late.

Some **adverbs show how** possible **or** certain **something is.**

It will definitely rain on Friday.

It will possibly rain on Friday.

It's going to rain.

It might rain, but it might not.

(3) **Write the adverbs below on the correct board.**

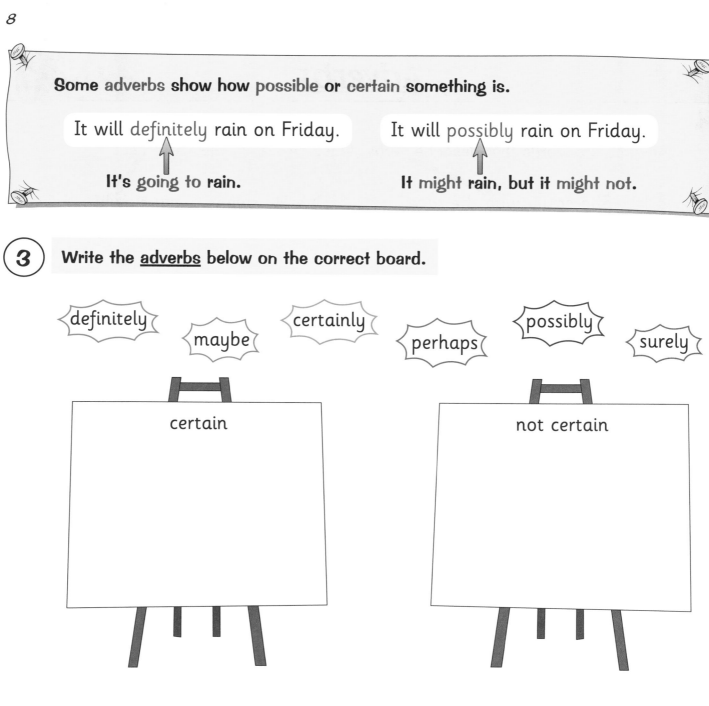

definitely   maybe   certainly   perhaps   possibly   surely

certain

not certain

(4) **Tick the boxes next to the sentences that sound certain.**
Then cross the boxes next to the sentences that are less certain.

Jared will <u>definitely</u> have a bigger portion than I will. ☐

<u>Perhaps</u> I'll go for a walk in the woods. ☐

My friends are <u>certainly</u> enjoying the party. ☐

<u>Maybe</u> the teacher will forget about our test. ☐

Humans will <u>possibly</u> live on Mars one day. ☐

5 Use the <u>adverbs</u> below to finish the sentences. Use each adverb <u>once</u>.

 probably   maybe   certainly    ~~definitely~~

The astronaut ......definitely...... needs her helmet in space.

I haven't seen Felix, but he's .... in the garden.

If you want to pass your exams, you must .... study.

.... we could go to the beach tomorrow.

6 Circle the <u>adverb</u> that makes each sentence <u>more certain</u>.

She is <u>certainly</u> / <u>maybe</u> going to win a gold medal.

Finn is <u>definitely</u> / <u>possibly</u> going to be a nurse.

<u>Perhaps</u> / <u>Surely</u> they won't be late.

That is <u>possibly</u> / <u>undoubtedly</u> a good book.

7 Add an <u>adverb</u> to the first sentence in each pair to make it sound <u>certain</u>.
Add a <u>different adverb</u> to the second sentence to make it sound <u>less certain</u>.

We are .... going to Greece in the summer.

We are .... going to Greece in the summer.

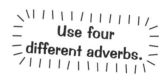 Use four different adverbs.

Fatima will .... play football this weekend.

Fatima will .... play football this weekend.

"I know what adverbs are and how to use them."

     Section 1 — Word Types

Pronouns

Pronouns are words that you use to **replace nouns.**

This is very repetitive.

Pedro made a sandwich and then Pedro ate the sandwich.

This is better. The pronouns **help you avoid repeating** 'Pedro' **and** 'the sandwich'.

Pedro made a sandwich and then he ate it.

---

1 **Underline the pronouns in each of the sentences below.**

There are two pronouns in each sentence.

Noah asked Verity if she wanted to play outside with him.

They stole our garden gnome and replaced it with a muddy boot.

We didn't go to the party because it started too late.

Bianca brought sweets for the class and shared them between us.

The postman delivers the post, but sometimes he brings it very late.

---

2 **Replace the underlined nouns with the correct pronouns.**

Khalid got mud on Saul's trousers, so he washed <u>the trousers</u> for <u>Saul</u>.

Stacey built a treehouse for Amy, then took <u>Amy</u> to play in <u>the treehouse</u>.

Paco and Julia found a secret cave, so <u>Paco and Julia</u> explored <u>the cave</u>.

Pronouns can be used across sentences as well.
They can make your writing flow better and make it easier to understand.

That's Cara's dad. He's taking her to school. ⟵ 'He' refers to Cara's dad and 'her' refers to Cara.

3 Use the <u>pronouns</u> below to finish the sentences. Use each pronoun <u>once</u>.

(he) (they) (we) (her) (it) (she) (him)

Mr Chang is a good teacher. .... makes our lessons really fun.

My brother and I are shopping. .... are buying a gift for our mum.

Dean and Samantha are mischievous. .... always get in trouble.

My best friend has a new baby sister. I can't wait to meet ....

Karl, my pen pal, lives in Germany. I write to .... once a week.

Annie borrowed my favourite jumper. I hope .... gives .... back.

4 Rewrite the <u>underlined</u> sentences, replacing the <u>nouns</u> with <u>pronouns</u>.

Nicky and Shane are in a band. <u>Nicky and Shane are really talented</u>.

Nicky and Shane are in a band. ....

Emilia really enjoyed the film. <u>Emilia wants to watch the film again</u>.

Emilia really enjoyed the film. ....

"I know what pronouns are and how to use them."

Section 1 — Word Types

Possessive Pronouns

Pronouns **are words that you use to** replace nouns.

Possessive pronouns **show** who **owns something.**

> Omar forgot his lunch, so Miriam let him share hers.

The possessive pronoun 'hers' is used instead of 'her lunch'. It shows that the lunch belongs **to Miriam.**

1 **Draw lines to match the possessive pronouns to the hook.**

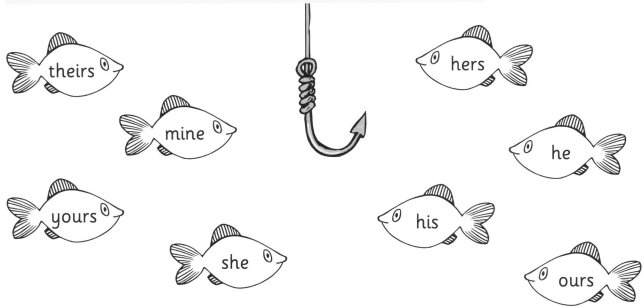

2 **Circle the correct possessive pronouns to complete the sentences below.**

My friend's dog is much smaller than mine / my.

I forgot my pens. Can I borrow yours / you?

Maria's car had broken down, so we took us / ours.

Aziz accidentally burst Priya's football, so he gave her them / his.

3 **Use the <u>pronouns</u> in the box below to fill in the sentences.**

| theirs | hers | mine | his | ours |

The cat belongs to Mina. The cat is ....

They bought a new sofa. The sofa is ....

I made a poster in school. The poster is ....

Safiya returned Ben's pen after school, because it was ....

Someone else sat in seats 8 and 9, although they were ....

4 **Answer the questions below using <u>his</u>, <u>hers</u> or <u>theirs</u>.**

Whose is the ice-cream?
The ice-cream is ....

Whose is the mug?
The mug is ....

Whose is the chess set?
The chess set is ....

Whose is the helmet?
The helmet is ....

"I know how to use possessive pronouns."

Relative Pronouns

Relative pronouns **are words like** 'who', 'whose' **and** 'which'.
They are used to join parts of sentences **together.**

> She's the astronaut who went to Mars. ⟵ 'who' **is used for** people

> I only wear jackets which are blue. ⟵ 'which' **is used for** things

1 **Draw lines through the correct** <u>relative pronoun</u> **to make complete sentences.**

I met a sailor   painted my room.

She's going to the shop   **which**   has sailed on every ocean.

They always go to places   sells motorbikes.

Rafael is the person   **who**   are warm and sunny.

2 **Use the** <u>relative pronouns</u> **below to finish the sentences.**

who   **whose**   **which**

My next door neighbour is the man .... owns the bakery.

We used to have a cat .... only had three legs.

That's the lady .... daughter is a scientist.

I like books .... are full of adventure.

> "I know how to use relative pronouns in my writing."

Section 1 — Word Types   *© CGP — not to be photocopied*

Articles and Determiners

Articles are the words 'a', 'an' and 'the'. They are determiners.

You use 'a' or 'an' for general things and 'the' for specific things.

> She would like a biscuit.

She wants any biscuit.

> She would like the chocolate biscuit.

She wants a particular biscuit.

Only use 'an' when the noun starts with a vowel sound. ➔ I'd like an apple, please.

---

1 **Underline the <u>articles</u> in the sentences below.**

I have a pet moose called Jared.

The bell rang, so we took a break.

All the teachers and the pupils went on a school trip.

I bought a new mug, but then I dropped it on the floor.

It's going to be an exciting day. We're going to the zoo.

Some of these sentences contain more than one article.

---

2 **Add <u>a</u>, <u>an</u> or <u>the</u> to the sentences below so that they make sense.**

There was .... beautiful sunset.

She is .... experienced helicopter pilot.

My friend has .... identical twin.

My dog is .... best dog in .... world.

When I was walking near .... River Avon, I saw .... otter.

Section 1 — Word Types

A **determiner** is any **word that goes before a** noun
to tell you whether it is general **or** specific.

Articles are the most common type of determiner**, but there are many more.**

I like that book.	I like this book.	I like some books.
I like those books.	I like these books.	I like every book.
I like my book.	I like your book.	I like her book.

(3) **Underline the determiners in the sentences below.**

I want to climb that mountain.

A secret agent caught those criminals.

The recipe says you need some sugar, eggs and flour.

Your grandad is standing beside that car.

 Some of these sentences contain more than one determiner.

(4) **Circle the correct determiners to complete the sentences below.**

Susan climbed out of her / these window.

Those / That birds are really loud.

Have you ever been to these / that restaurant?

Nazia is looking for some / an old photos.

John really enjoyed reading those / this books about spaceships.

This / A cake is the tastiest cake I've ever eaten.

"I know what determiners are and how to use them."

Clauses

Most sentences are made of clauses.

A **main clause** has a **subject** and a **verb**, and **makes sense** on its own.

The **subject** is the person or thing **doing** the verb. → Carolina played with the children.

The **verb** usually **comes after** the subject.

A **subordinate clause** gives extra information, but it **doesn't make sense** on its own.

main clause ⟹ Peter went fishing when it was raining. ⟸ subordinate clause

1 Underline the **verb** in each of these sentences.

The car skidded around the corner.

Erin did her homework before school.

Farmer Gregory bought some goats.

The grumpy llama chased the hikers.

The bats flew out of the cave.

Mila the cat ate the whole fish.

2 Tick the sentences where the **subject** is **underlined**.

I gave some cookies to <u>Ingrid</u>. ☐   <u>Nobody</u> knew what to say. ☐

<u>Taio</u> dug a hole in the sand. ☐   Can I have a <u>drink</u>, please? ☐

<u>My neighbour</u> is an acrobat. ☐   <u>We</u> went to see the doctor. ☐

He <u>slammed</u> the door shut. ☐   The lamb bleated <u>quietly</u>. ☐

3 Label the underlined part of each sentence as either <u>subject</u> or <u>verb</u>.

<u>The monkey</u> watched the tourists.

My aunt Marta <u>made</u> the cake.

Jason and Mario <u>hummed</u> a tune.

<u>A swarm of bees</u> buzzed around us.

4 Draw lines to match each <u>clause</u> to the <u>correct label</u>.

we walked the dog

if he has time

Graeme was sent home

the music was loud

as they ate the food

main clause

subordinate clause

he will come to visit us

when the party started

after she hit Jo

the pigs snorted loudly

before I had dinner

5 Tick the sentences where the <u>subordinate clause</u> is <u>underlined</u>.

The alarm beeped <u>until I turned it off</u>.

Since it was dark, <u>Lola had a torch with her</u>.

<u>We cover our ears</u> when she starts singing.

You need to tell me <u>where you hid the toys</u>.

I can have a puppy <u>provided that I take care of it</u>.

Even if I knew, <u>I wouldn't tell you the answer</u>.

6 Underline the <u>main clause</u> in each sentence below. One has been done for you.

<u>The mouse ran away</u> when it saw the cat.

After he found the treasure, the pirate stole it.

Before I go to bed, I brush my teeth.

Colette watered the flowers because it was hot.

I climbed the tree although I was scared.

7 Draw lines to match each <u>main clause</u> on the left with the correct <u>subordinate clause</u> on the right.

I will wrap his presents

She cleaned her shoes

I asked for a hot drink

as it was cold outside.

while he's at school.

because they were muddy.

8 Add a word from the box and your own <u>subordinate clause</u> to complete the sentences below.

when   ~~after~~   if   until

Only use each word from the box <u>once</u>.

You can have dessert ...... after you have finished your main meal.

Leo will come over ....

We can go to the cinema ....

Don't open your presents ....

"I can spot main clauses and subordinate clauses."

Section 2 — Clauses and Phrases

Relative Clauses

A relative clause **is a** subordinate clause **that is often introduced by a** relative pronoun.

> This is the bag <u>which</u> you gave me.

relative pronoun

relative clause

The words that, which, whose and who are all relative pronouns.

The words where **and** when **can also introduce relative clauses.** ⟶ Bolton is the town <u>where</u> I was born.

---

1 **Underline the <u>relative pronoun</u> in each sentence.**

She hid the book that I was looking for.

Hamish is the child who lives next door.

We went to the shop which sells fudge.

We heard a musician who is very talented.

I have a letter which is addressed to you.

---

2 **Tick the sentences where the <u>relative clause</u> is <u>underlined</u>.**

<u>I drank the milkshake</u> that Ella had made for herself. ☐

Mr Plump is the man <u>who teaches history</u>. ☐

We watched TV <u>when we should have been asleep</u>. ☐

<u>Jessica painted the picture</u> which is over there. ☐

Robbie was shocked <u>when we surprised him</u>. ☐

<u>I warned you about it</u> when I saw you last week. ☐

---

3 Underline the <u>relative clause</u> in each sentence.

Hazel swatted the fly that was annoying her.

Nobody saw the children who broke the window.

There's some food in the kitchen which I saved for you.

Margot is the woman whose dogs tried to bite me.

4 Complete the sentences below with '<u>who</u>' or '<u>which</u>'.
The first one has been done for you.

Anna made a cake ......<u>which</u>...... had chocolate icing.

Marco shouted at Billy, ... was pulling silly faces.

I looked for the football .... we had lost.

We bought a car .... used to belong to a celebrity.

Mum helped the old lady .... had fallen over.

5 Draw lines to join the <u>main</u> and <u>relative clauses</u> using the
<u>correct relative pronoun</u>. The first one has been done for you.

Kim sent me a birthday card | who | fur is black and white.

My cat has a kitten | which | thinks he's a wizard.

Seth has lots of books | whose | had blue flowers on it.

I saw the mysterious man | that | he has never read.

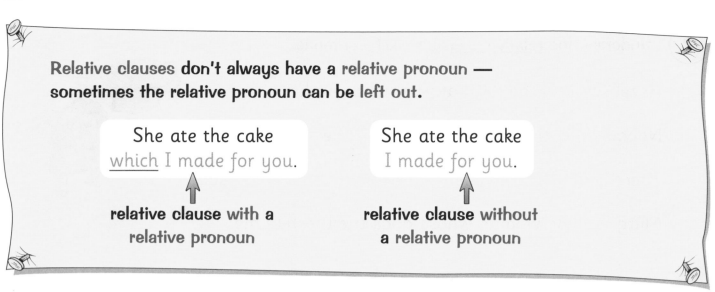

Relative clauses **don't always have a** relative pronoun —
sometimes the relative pronoun can be left out.

> She ate the cake
> <u>which</u> I made for you.
>
> relative clause **with a**
> relative pronoun

> She ate the cake
> I made for you.
>
> relative clause **without**
> a relative pronoun

6 Circle the <u>relative pronoun</u> that can be <u>removed</u> from each sentence.

Are these the flowers that we planted last year?

Here is the blanket which we took on the picnic.

There's the man who I spoke to yesterday.

Did you find the shoes which you were looking for?

7 Underline the <u>relative clause</u> in each of the sentences below.

He cleaned up the mess he had made.

She chose the dress she wanted.

Jim told me a story I'd already heard.

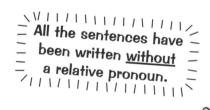

All the sentences have been written <u>without</u> a relative pronoun.

8 Rewrite the sentence below <u>without</u> the <u>relative pronoun</u>.

I think it's time that I went home.

....

"I can spot sentences with relative clauses."

Phrases

Clauses and sentences are made up of groups of words called phrases.

A phrase either doesn't have a verb, or doesn't have a subject (some phrases might have neither).

two soft, sparkly cushions   in the middle of the ocean

1 Write a 'P' next to the <u>phrases</u> and a 'C' next to the <u>clauses</u>.

they caught the chicken ☐   the sea glinted ☐

as quickly as possible ☐   before midnight ☐

to the seaside ☐   the old grey dog ☐

extremely annoying ☐   my parrot can talk ☐

2 Draw lines to match each group of words to the correct label.

they speak Spanish   the colourful shell

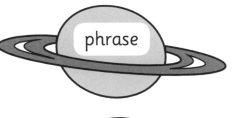

near the supermarket   she borrowed a pen

I used to play chess   a lemon lollipop

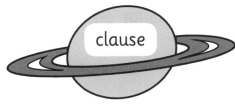

the stars are shining   next to the chair

"I can spot phrases and clauses."

Noun Phrases

A noun phrase is a phrase that acts as a noun.
Noun phrases add extra information to a sentence. → the angry bull

A noun phrase can have
adjectives, prepositions
and more than one noun.

the angry white bull in the field

adjectives   noun   preposition   noun

1 Circle the <u>noun</u> in the underlined <u>noun phrases</u> below.

Kate used <u>three red and white ribbons</u> to make the bows.

<u>The small, fluffy lamb</u> was born yesterday.

The chef used <u>the shiniest red tomatoes</u> for the sauce.

Nathan cautiously sniffed <u>the sticky mixture</u>.

<u>The bright red light</u> flickered in the darkness.

2 Add your own <u>adjectives</u> to complete the <u>noun phrases</u>
below. Use the pictures on the right to help you.

the .... giraffe with a knot in its neck

the .... sailor on the tiny boat

the .... penguin with the hat and gloves

"I can use noun phrases."

Co-ordinating Conjunctions

Co-ordinating conjunctions **are words that** join **two** main clauses **together.**
Use FANBOYS to remember them: For And Nor But Or Yet So

I went to the zoo <u>and</u> I saw a lion.

main clause   co-ordinating conjunction   main clause

1 **Underline the <u>co-ordinating conjunction</u> in each sentence.**

Georgie likes dogs, but she doesn't like frogs.

I was sleepy, for it had been a busy day.

Rahman was hungry, so he ate an apple.

It was dark outside, yet Wiktoria wanted to go for a walk.

We can play on the slide or we can play on the see-saw.

He likes pink and he likes purple.

2 **Choose a <u>word</u> from the box to complete the sentences.**

Only use each
word once.

but   so   or   for

I'm going to the shops, ... I need to buy some bananas.

They are tired, ... they don't want to go to sleep.

I have hurt my leg, ... I can't play outside.

We can go home .... we can go to see the palace.

"I can use co-ordinating conjunctions."

Subordinating Conjunctions

Subordinating conjunctions **are words that** link a main clause to a subordinate clause. **They can go at the** start **of a sentence or in the middle.**

He likes to sing <u>while</u> he is cleaning.

main clause   subordinating conjunction   subordinate clause

1 **Underline the <u>subordinating conjunction</u> in each sentence.**

We can play a game while we wait.

Although it is not raining, he has brought an umbrella.

You can stay for tea unless you want to go home.

Since she caught a cold, she has been unable to talk.

After you tidy up, you can play video games.

I want to stay awake until I see a shooting star.

2 **Draw lines to connect the <u>clauses</u> to the correct <u>subordinating conjunction</u>.**

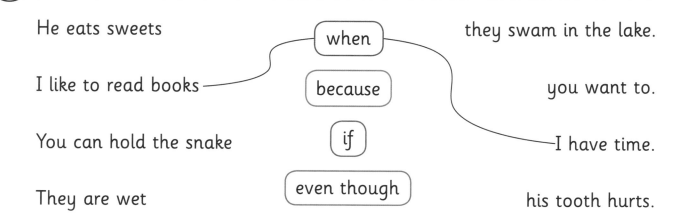

He eats sweets   when   they swam in the lake.

I like to read books   because   you want to.

You can hold the snake   if   I have time.

They are wet   even though   his tooth hurts.

"I can use subordinating conjunctions."

Using Conjunctions for Cohesion

Conjunctions **can help your writing** flow **better — this is called** cohesion.

It was sunny. We went to the park. We had a picnic. ← **This** doesn't **flow very well.**

It was sunny so we went to the park and we had a picnic. ← **This** flows **much better.**

1 **Circle the correct** <u>conjunction</u> **to make a full sentence.**

Riya wants pizza for tea <u>or</u> / <u>but</u> Laura wants spaghetti.

I don't like Zach <u>because</u> / <u>while</u> he broke my bicycle.

He finished his homework <u>since</u> / <u>before</u> he went to play outside.

At the fair, we went on the waltzers <u>and</u> / <u>when</u> we ate candyfloss.

2 **Choose one of the conjunctions below to** <u>join</u> **the sentences** <u>together</u>.

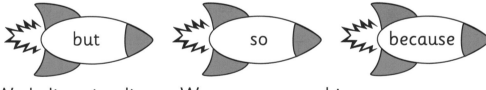

but   so   because   Only use each word once.

We believe in aliens. We saw a spaceship.

....

I bought you a present. I forgot it.

....

She was cold. She put on a jumper.

....

"I can use conjunctions to make my writing flow."

Prepositions

Prepositions **tell you** where, when or why **something happens.**

I go to my dad's house on Tuesdays.

where   when

They can also tell you when **things happen** in relation **to each other.**

He brushed his teeth before bed.

(1) **Choose the correct <u>preposition</u> from the box to complete the sentences.**

in	on	next to	under

The boat is .... the island.

The octopus is .... the sea.

The pirate is .... the island.

The treasure is .... the tree.

(2) **Underline the <u>preposition</u> in each sentence.**

Some prepositions are made up of more than one word.

Tanya, Halima and Max are meeting at the park.

We eventually found the clue hidden above the door.

I found some smelly socks underneath my bed.

They will see the statue before going home.

She is travelling from her house.

He couldn't see because she was standing in front of the TV.

3 Underline the <u>preposition</u> in each sentence. Then draw lines to show whether the preposition tells you <u>where</u> or <u>when</u> something happens.

I have a piano lesson until 2:30 pm.

They went home after the film.

The park is behind the school.

He has been dancing since this morning.

My sister said we can go to the theme park.

where

when

4 Circle the correct <u>preposition</u> to make a full sentence.

We haven't seen her <u>since</u> / <u>while</u> last week.

<u>From</u> / <u>Before</u> eating, they wash their hands.

I had a painful headache <u>under</u> / <u>during</u> the show.

He was playing <u>because of</u> / <u>until</u> teatime.

5 Use <u>prepositions</u> to write three sentences that describe the <u>location</u> of <u>three things</u> in the picture.

....

....

....

....

....

"I can choose and use prepositions."

Section 3 — Conjunctions and Prepositions

Section 4 — Linking Ideas

Linking Ideas in a Paragraph

Adverbial phrases **tell you** how, when, where **or** how often **something happens.**
They can help your writing to flow **more smoothly.**

Yesterday morning it was raining, but by lunchtime it had stopped.

The adverbial phrases **help this sentence to** flow
by telling you about when **something happened.**

1 **Underline the <u>adverbial phrase</u> in each sentence.**

Let's go for a walk after lunch.

I can run unbelievably fast.

He walks the dog twice a day.

There's fruit on the table.

Every weekend we go to town.

She stroked the rabbit very gently.

Kate cycled home really slowly.

The class was quiet this morning.

Ziyad is in his room.

I found my sock inside my shoe.

2 **Draw lines from each adverbial phrase to show whether they
give information about <u>how</u>, <u>when</u> or <u>where</u> something happens.**

next week

almost perfectly

in the garden

extremely quickly

under the door mat

much earlier

how

where

when

by tomorrow

with a big smile

on the floor

very quietly

last night

near the bookshelf

3 Complete the sentences by choosing a <u>phrase</u> from the clouds below.

under the bed   so loudly   this afternoon

\\\\ // / / / / / /
Only use each
phrase once.
/ / \ \ \ \ \ \ \ \ \

every weekend   by 12 o'clock   next to the bank

I like to go cycling ....

Her brother was playing music ....

There is a nice book shop ....

We are going to bake cookies ....

She thinks there is a monster ....

All of the cake had been eaten ....

4 Circle the correct <u>adverbial phrases</u> in each sentence below.

We are going on holiday <u>in three days</u> / <u>yesterday morning</u> .

<u>On Saturday morning</u> / <u>Last weekend</u> , I am going to visit my cousins.

They are going to stay in a villa <u>just under</u> / <u>next to</u> the beach.

My sister Jannat can swim <u>very poorly</u> / <u>really well</u> .

<u>Since then</u> / <u>After that</u> , you will be hungry.

We usually visit my grandparents <u>once a month</u> / <u>the other day</u> .

He looked at me <u>with an angry scowl</u> / <u>unbelievably loudly</u> .

"I can link ideas together using adverbial phrases."

Section 4 — Linking Ideas

Linking Paragraphs

You can use adverbs **and other** adverbial phrases **to link paragraphs together.**

I had been waiting to go out and fly my kite all morning, but the rain kept pouring. That afternoon, the storm finally ended and the sun came out through the clouds.

Adverbs and adverbial phrases can be used to show a change **in** time, place **or** number.

In the hall, my wellies were waiting by the door. I quickly pulled them on and rushed outside, my kite grasped tightly in my hand.

1 Write the words and phrases below in the correct box to show whether they give a change in <u>time</u>, <u>place</u> or <u>number</u>.

firstly   on the roof   next month   in the morning   at the bus stop

earlier   secondly   in the kitchen   under the chair   fourthly

thirdly   behind the cushion   later that day   last year

Place	Number
....	....
....	....
....	....
....	....

Time
....
....

2 **Use each of the <u>words</u> or <u>phrases</u> below to link these paragraphs.**

Inside   With a big yawn   All of a sudden   In the garden

Jasper the dog lay in the kitchen, snoozing in his basket as the sun came in through the window.

...................................., Alvin was cooking sausages on the barbecue. They were almost ready to eat, and they sizzled as he turned them.

...................................., he heard a shout from inside the house. Abandoning the barbecue, he ran inside to find out what was happening.

...................................., Suzie and Harmony were having an argument. They were shouting so loudly that they woke Jasper up from his nap.

...................................., Jasper got up from his basket. His nose began to twitch as the delicious smell of sausages floated in from the garden.

3 **Write the <u>first two sentences</u> of the next paragraph in the story, <u>starting</u> with an <u>adverbial phrase</u>. Underline your <u>adverbial phrase</u> once you've finished it.**

One morning, Charlie the chimp was feeling restless. He was bored of the jungle, and wanted to go on an adventure.

....

....

....

"I can link paragraphs using adverbial phrases."

Section 4 — Linking Ideas

Section 5 — Verb Tenses

Present Tense and Past Tense

Use the present tense to write about something that happens regularly.

> Tina cycles to school.
> We visit our aunt.

Use the past tense to write about something that's finished.

> Tina cycled to school.
> We visited our aunt.

To make most verbs into the past tense, add 'ed' on the end.

1 **Tick the box to show whether each sentence is in the past or the present tense.**

	Past	Present		Past	Present
Omar <u>makes</u> scones.	☐	☐	Chelsea <u>does</u> karate.	☐	☐
Luke <u>studies</u> hard.	☐	☐	Ty <u>finished</u> the pizza.	☐	☐
Nora <u>went</u> out.	☐	☐	Louise <u>gave</u> a speech.	☐	☐

2 **Put these <u>present tense</u> verbs in brackets into the <u>past tense</u>.**

Some of these verbs don't follow the 'ed' rule.

This evening, I (cook) .... chilli for my family.

Ellen (plays) .... the drums for the school band.

The teacher said that you (work) .... hard.

Layton (runs) .... a long way today.

We (do) .... all our homework on Saturday.

"I can use the present and past tenses."

Verbs with 'ing'

If you want to write about something that's still happening, you need to use the present form of 'to be' plus the main verb with 'ing' on the end.

to be verb ing

I am thinking.   You are fighting.   He is meeting new people.

'ing' verbs in the past are formed with 'to be' in the past tense.

They were calling.   She was looking at the photos.

1 Draw lines to complete the sentences using the **correct** form of '**to be**'.

Maria .... cooking.

We .... watching.

They .... playing.

He .... singing.

 are

 am

 is

The boys .... talking.

Ravi and I .... eating.

You .... shouting.

I .... going.

2 Complete these sentences using the **present tense** form of '**to be**' and a **verb** on the clipboard **with 'ing' added**.

Zoya .... a robot.

We .... a theme park.

Sid .... a sausage roll.

You .... for your keys.

I .... very sleepy now.

build   feel

look

buy

visit

3 Draw lines to show whether each sentence is in the present tense with 'ing' or the past tense with 'ing'.

I was telling Noor.

Troy was making toast.

Arjun is sleeping deeply.

You are leaving today.

Present tense with 'ing'

Past tense with 'ing'

I was sitting there.

Gabrielle is smiling.

They were feeling excited.

We are taking a break.

4 Fill in the gaps in the table.

Present tense with 'ing'	Past tense with 'ing'
Jade is calling Beth.	Jade was calling Beth.
....	Amir was going bowling.
They are having lunch.	....
We are starting a project.	....
....	You were reading a book.

5 Rewrite these sentences with the correct form of the verb in brackets to make the past tense with 'ing'.

Whiskers ➕ (to be) ➕ (to break) Granny's plates.

....

We ➕ (to be) ➕ (to ask) for pudding.

....

"I can use verbs in their 'ing' forms."

Past Tense with 'have'

Use the past tense with 'have' to talk about something that happened recently. To form this, you need the present form of the verb 'to have'.

I have talked to Laura.   He has moved house.

This is called the present perfect tense.

The verb after 'to have' is usually in the normal past tense form, but not always.

She has gone home.   not 'she has went home'

---

1) Tick the correct box to show whether each sentence is missing '<u>has</u>' or '<u>have</u>'.

	has	have			has	have
You .... looked.	☐	☐	He .... decided.		☐	☐
Sana .... asked.	☐	☐	The dog .... barked.		☐	☐
We .... built.	☐	☐	They .... washed.		☐	☐
Gethin .... been.	☐	☐	I .... remembered.		☐	☐

---

2) Circle the correct form of the <u>verb</u> for the <u>past tense with 'have'</u> in each of the sentences below.

Jack has <u>stay</u> / <u>stayed</u> at home with Vanessa.

Alice and Maisie have <u>raised</u> / <u>raise</u> their hands.

I have <u>waits</u> / <u>waited</u> for this parcel for ages.

We have <u>says</u> / <u>said</u> that we will go together.

They have <u>made</u> / <u>make</u> a mess with their rubbish.

Rosie has <u>buys</u> / <u>bought</u> too much milk.

Section 5 — Verb Tenses

3 Put these present tense verbs into the past tense with 'have'.

Present tense	Past tense with 'have'
I reach	I ....
he turns	he ....
we want	we ....
you try	you ....
they use	they ....

4 Fill the gaps below with the words in boxes to make the past tense with 'have'.

have offered   lost   have discovered   grown   has played

Ariana has .... her father's watch.

Julian .... a tennis match today.

I .... to pay for the concert tickets.

We have .... vegetables in the garden.

I .... some hidden treasure.

5 Write a sentence using the past tense with 'have' of the verbs in the boxes.

play   ....

talk   ....

"I can use the past tense with 'have'."

Staying in the Same Tense

The verbs in a sentence should usually be in the same tense.

> We walked up the mountain and sat at the top. ⟵ past tense

> present tense ⟶ We go to art lessons and learn to draw.

1 Draw lines to match the **pairs of phrases** that are in the **same tense**.

(I jumped) (you have answered) (they are waiting) (he drinks)

(I have asked) (she eats) (you hopped) (we are running)

2 The underlined word in each sentence is in the **wrong tense**. Write it in the **correct tense** on the line.

The teacher goes to the board and <u>wrote</u> the date. ....

David met Harley in the park and they <u>plays</u> for an hour. ....

Mum is chopping a carrot because she <u>makes</u> a stew. ....

I played video games for a while before I <u>am going</u> to bed. ....

3 Write a sentence using the **verbs** below that keeps them both in the **same tense**.

(turn) (open)

....

"I can stay in the right tense in my writing."

Standard and Non-Standard English

Standard English **is the** formal **type of writing you should use in your work. It helps to make your writing** clearer.

Standard English ⇒ You are joking. | I saw you earlier.

Non-Standard English ⇒ You is joking. | I seen you earlier.

1 Draw lines to show whether these sentences are written in <u>Standard English</u> or <u>non-Standard English</u>.

Standard English

They have been out.

It were awful.

I have did my best.

You are funny.

It was wonderful.

We is making lunch.

Freddie like the biscuits.

She made a cake.

non-Standard English

2 Fill in the gaps in the sentences using '<u>I</u>' or '<u>me</u>'.

.... think the sweets look yummy.

Grace pushed .... over in the playground.

Would you like to be friends with .... ?

Ifran and .... like playing wheelchair tennis.

The teacher told .... off for talking.

3 Tick the box under <u>them</u> or <u>those</u> to complete the sentences in Standard English.

them those

Please put .... wrappers in the bin. ☐ ☐

.... two are playing on the beach. ☐ ☐

I will show .... the canteen. ☐ ☐

He has finally found .... ☐ ☐

Who do .... bags belong to? ☐ ☐

4 Draw lines to match each sentence with its <u>Standard English</u> form.

I done it yesterday.   My mum gave me £10.

She has went home.   We were really hungry.

My mum give me £10.   She has gone home.

We was really hungry.   I did it yesterday.

5 The <u>underlined verb</u> in each sentence is <u>incorrect</u>.
Rewrite each one <u>correctly</u> on the lines below.

Write the verb in the present tense.

He <u>are</u> at school today. ⟹ ....

She <u>go</u> to the shops. ⟹ ....

They <u>is</u> angry with you. ⟹ ....

I don't <u>knows</u> how to do it. ⟹ ....

We <u>wants</u> to see the film. ⟹ ....

Section 6 — Standard and Non-Standard English

In **Standard English**, **only use** one negative word to make the meaning negative. ⟹ I didn't see anything.

Double negatives are non-Standard English. ⟹ I didn't see nothing.

'Ain't' is also non-Standard English. We ain't seen it. ⟹ We haven't seen it.

---

(6) Circle the correct word to complete the <u>negative sentences</u> below.

I couldn't see <u>nobody</u> / <u>anybody</u>.

They can't play outside <u>no more</u> / <u>anymore</u>.

He can't find the dog <u>anywhere</u> / <u>nowhere</u>.

Don't tell <u>no one</u> / <u>anyone</u> about the surprise.

---

(7) Tick the boxes next to the sentences which are written using <u>Standard English</u>.

We can't touch nothing. ☐   She doesn't speak to nobody. ☐

They don't like animals. ☐   They were nowhere to be seen. ☐

I didn't get no presents. ☐   I can't hear anything. ☐

---

(8) Rewrite the sentence below using <u>Standard English</u>.

He ain't talking to me.

....

"I can use Standard English in my work."

Capital Letters and Full Stops

Sentences always **start** with a **capital letter** and often **finish** with a **full stop**.

Sentences with a **full stop** are often **statements**.

A statement is a sentence that tells you something.

Use **capital letters** for **I** and for **names** of people, places or things.

This Sunday, I would like to go to Newcastle.

---

1 Tick the words that should have **capital letters**.

yellow ☐   january ☐   haircut ☐

martin ☐   town ☐   russia ☐

---

2 Circle all the letters that should be **capital letters** in the passage below.

andrea and saul met for lunch in manchester on tuesday.

they talked about the easter holidays. saul had been to

portugal with his friend, emma, to see his favourite band.

---

3 Rewrite these sentences with **capital letters** and **full stops** in the correct places.

my cousin, charlotte, owns her own business

....

in edinburgh, i went to three museums

....

"I can use capital letters and full stops in sentences."

Question Marks

Questions always end with a **question mark** and often begin with a **question word**.

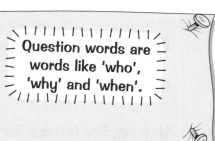
Question words are words like 'who', 'why' and 'when'.

Who **is that?**

When **did you go?**

---

1 Underline the **question words** in the sentences below.

Which pair of shoes do you prefer?

Whose lunchbox has been left on the stairs?

How can we explain this?

Where should we go for lunch tomorrow?

Who won the volleyball tournament?

---

2 Write a **full stop** or a **question mark** in each box to complete these sentences **correctly**.

Let's go to the cinema to see that new film ☐

Would you like to go shopping with me this weekend ☐

I enjoy exploring new places with my friends ☐

Playing football is my favourite thing to do ☐

How do you know the people you were talking to ☐

Would you like lasagne for dinner tonight ☐

"I can use question marks correctly."

Exclamation Marks

Exclamation marks **show that something is said loudly or with strong emotion.** ➡️ That's fantastic!

Exclamation marks are also used for **strong commands.** ➡️ Leave me alone!

If the command **isn't urgent or strong, use a full stop.** ➡️ Tie your shoes.

1 Tick the sentences that are most likely to end with an **exclamation mark**.

I'd like some toast ☐   What a masterpiece ☐

Put that down, now ☐   Do you need a break ☐

How dare you ☐   Don't talk nonsense ☐

2 Use a **full stop** or an **exclamation mark** to complete each sentence below.

Please make a shopping list .....   Come here immediately .....

I was absolutely terrified .....   You need to walk the dog .....

3 Write two sentences using some words from the box and an **exclamation mark**.

cheerful   annoying   person   song

....

....

"I can use exclamation marks correctly."

Sentence Practice

Remember — sentences should always start with a capital letter.

They can end with a full stop, a question mark or an exclamation mark.

| Ben ran away. | What are you doing? | Give it to me! |

1 Draw lines to match each sentence with its **description**.

Collect your bags from the classroom.

Thomas and Kara are my friends.

Why do we have to get up so early?

What a big dog that is!

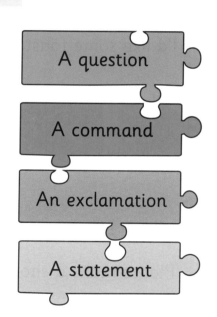

A question

A command

An exclamation

A statement

2 Write the most likely **final punctuation** in each box.

Have you ever built a sandcastle on the beach ☐

How long and boring this journey is ☐

Where would you like to go on holiday this year ☐

Sandra has always enjoyed playing hockey ☐

Give them their sandwiches back at once ☐

3 These passages are missing <u>full stops</u> and <u>capital letters</u>. Add <u>full stops</u> in the <u>correct</u> places and circle the letters that should be <u>capital letters</u>.

two years ago, i went skiing in austria with my family we were away for five days between christmas and new year my brother learned how to snowboard with an instructor called kelly

miss west is my english teacher she always has a smile on her face she used to live in new zealand, but now she lives in kent she's bringing her rabbit, called hoppy, to school on friday

4 Write a <u>sentence</u> about each of the pictures below, ending with the <u>punctuation mark</u> in the box.

➕ (!) ....

➕ (?) ....

➕ (.) ....

"I can punctuate sentences correctly."

Section 7 — Sentence Punctuation

Section 8 — Commas

Commas in Lists

Commas **are used to** separate items in a list.

You need commas **between all the things in the list except the** last two.
You need to put 'and' or 'or' between the last two things.

> I ate three apples, two bananas, an orange and some grapes.

---

1 Read these sentences then write the name of the person who used <u>commas correctly</u>.

Jacob   "I went camping with my dad, aunt and cousin."

Clara   "I found, stones shells and a fossil, at the beach."

Yayah   "I bought a game, sweets, and some, new shoes."

.... used commas correctly.

---

2 Each sentence is missing one <u>comma</u>. Write the comma in the <u>correct box</u>.

The weather tomorrow [ ] will be cloudy [ ] windy and [ ] rainy.

I will [ ] be able to visit on [ ] Friday [ ] Saturday or Sunday.

Would you like apple [ ] orange [ ] or [ ] blackcurrant juice?

We will see Martha [ ] Levi and Rhys [ ] at the [ ] after school club.

Shall we go to France [ ] Spain or Italy [ ] on holiday [ ] this year?

---

3 **Add <u>commas</u> in the correct places in these sentences.**

I like toffees fudge caramels and peppermints.

Hamsters rabbits gerbils and guinea pigs are all good pets.

The bracelet was covered in emeralds rubies and diamonds.

Mars Jupiter and Venus are all planets near to Earth.

My friends' birthdays are in January March and June.

I took part in the long jump hurdles sprint and relay.

4 **Complete the <u>lists</u> using the phrases in the <u>boxes</u>. Remember to put the <u>commas</u> in the <u>correct places</u>.**

| walk to school | ride my bike | do karate | and play fetch with my dog |

To keep fit, I ....

....

....

| learn my lines | make my costume | practise my song | and sell some tickets |

Before the school play, I need to ....

....

....

"I can use commas to separate items in a list."

Section 8 — Commas

Commas to Join Sentences

You can use a **comma** with a **FANBOYS** conjunction
(for, and, nor, but, or, yet, so) to join two sentences together.

I saw Mia. We talked. ⟹ I saw Mia, and we talked.

Remember — you only need a comma if you're joining main clauses that could stand alone. For example, this sentence doesn't need a comma:

I saw Mia and then went out. ⟵ The second clause doesn't work as a sentence on its own.

1 Put a tick next to the sentences which use <u>commas</u> correctly.

I am beginning to feel ill so, I am going home. ☐

He is, a good painter, but he is, a great poet. ☐

We are tired, yet we want to stay awake until midnight. ☐

I am going to the supermarket, for I have run out of milk. ☐

Your work is good, and, you have earned a gold star. ☐

I can watch television, or I can play video games. ☐

2 Add a <u>comma</u> before the <u>conjunction</u> in the sentences that need them.

I like puzzles so I do one every night.

I'll have the ham and pineapple pizza please.

I must go now or I will be late again.

I went to the shop but didn't buy anything.

3 Choose a <u>conjunction</u> from the ring to complete each sentence.

Use each conjunction only once.

Kirsty played netball, ... she scored seven goals.

We could cook dinner, ... we could order takeaway.

The forecast predicted rain, ... Elijah wore his coat.

Jasmine waited for the bus, ... the bus did not come.

but   so
        or
and

4 Each sentence is missing <u>one comma</u>. Write the <u>comma</u> in the <u>correct box</u>.

Jake did not bring a ☐ pen today ☐ nor did he bring ☐ a pencil.

I want to read a new ☐ book ☐ for I have read the book ☐ I have.

We are hungry ☐ yet we cannot eat ☐ anything ☐ until lunchtime.

There was a great ☐ sale ☐ so I bought ☐ twenty pairs of socks!

5 Rewrite the sentences using a <u>comma</u> and the <u>conjunction</u> to join each pair.

Zia planted seeds. They grew quickly.

(and)   ....

We guessed the answer. It was wrong.

(but)   ....

The view was great. I took a photo.

(so)   ....

"I can use commas to join sentences."

Section 8 — Commas

Commas After Introductions

You need to put a comma after adverbial phrases at the start of sentences. Adverbial phrases usually tell you when or where something happens:

Last week, we got a trampoline.   In London, I saw the Prime Minister.

They can also tell you how or how often something happens:

As quickly as possible, I turned around.   Every day, I feed the cat.

1 Tick the sentences which use commas correctly.

In ten years, I want to be a successful Olympic gymnast. ☐

On Hallie's birthday she went to a restaurant, for dinner. ☐

An hour ago, the postman brought a parcel for me. ☐

In the countryside you often see, sheep, cows and horses. ☐

Once a week, I have to babysit my cousin Alannah. ☐

2 Write the correct adverbial phrases in these sentences below.

| in silence | at weekends |
| in France | in prehistoric times |

Remember to put commas in the correct places.

.... humans made useful tools out of rocks.

.... the class work hard at their reading test.

.... Lea tried croissants and jam for breakfast.

.... Spenser helps his dad wash the car.

3 Add <u>commas</u> in the <u>correct</u> places in the sentences below.

With great care I checked whether any cars were approaching.

As slowly as possible Jason walked towards the door.

During Queen Victoria's reign women usually wore dresses.

In Edinburgh I saw a huge, old castle on a hill.

The day after tomorrow Ali is going to play badminton with me.

Every morning Brooke eats breakfast and then brushes her teeth.

4 Use the boxes below to make sentences that <u>start</u> with an <u>adverbial phrase</u>.

I found   ,   Under the sofa   an old letter.

....

,   her dog.   Sophia walks   Every day

....

5 Write your own sentence using the <u>adverbial phrase</u> below. Use the picture to help you.

After the show ....

....

"I can use commas after introductions."

Section 8 — Commas

Commas for Extra Information

Commas can also be used to separate extra information in a sentence.

My alarm, which was set for 7 o'clock, went off.

The sentence should still make sense when the extra information is removed. → My alarm went off.

1 Put a tick next to the sentences which use commas correctly.

The book, which was the third, in the series was fantastic. ☐

The baker, Mr Miller, saved me my favourite sandwich. ☐

I visited Natalia, a childhood friend, when I went to Devon. ☐

Rhys, who is two years older than me is really tall. ☐

My village, which is tiny, has hardly any shops. ☐

2 Draw lines to create sentences that include a piece of extra information.

The wooden ship,	which is difficult,	on Saturdays.
The firefighters,	my favourite food,	to get to school.
We have sausages,	which was really old,	came to help.
Umar cycles uphill,	Kit and Cara,	was sinking.

3 Add <u>commas</u> in the correct places in the <u>sentences</u> below.

The pupils whose names were Erica and Scott got detentions.

Harley the youngest player was allowed the first turn.

Ben learnt about Egypt where the pyramids are in History.

Amara's two rabbits Primrose and Bluebell are very cute.

Dinner which is spaghetti and meatballs is at 6 o'clock.

The concert which I am really excited about is on Friday.

4 Rewrite the <u>sentences</u> below, adding the <u>extra information</u> in the boxes. Use <u>commas</u> where they are needed.

My teacher knows lots about maths. | whose name is Miss Brooks |

....

....

The new cinema has just opened. | which is on the main road |

....

....

The Eiffel Tower is in Paris. | which is a famous landmark |

....

....

"I can use commas to separate extra information."

Section 8 — Commas

Comma Practice

Use commas:

for lists	You can have water, milk or juice.
to join sentences	I haven't got the time, nor do I have the money.
after adverbial phrases	In May, I rode a horse.
for extra information	Dan, my brother, is twelve in November.

1 Put a tick next to the sentences which use <u>commas</u> correctly and a cross next to the ones which <u>don't</u>. Three sentences are incorrect.

In summer, I like to go swimming in the ocean. ☐

My favourite colours are purple blue, and orange. ☐

I go to the restaurant, and I order a steak. ☐

My friends Nia and Li are having a joint birthday party. ☐

In the future cars might be able to drive themselves. ☐

2 Finish the sentence with a list using the <u>phrases</u> on the <u>to-do list</u>. Remember to use <u>commas</u> correctly.

Today I need to ....

....

....

....

To do

tidy my room

do my homework

feed my pet snake

ring Grandad

3 Complete the sentences using the <u>options below</u>. Use each option <u>once</u>. Remember to add <u>commas</u> where they are needed.

| a famous statue | At low tide | Richard and Michael |

| With great care | In autumn | who was very light |

.... Tamika went looking for starfish.

Kevin .... was good at the pole vault.

The Angel of the North .... is in Gateshead.

.... Hassan completed the science experiment.

.... I love watching the leaves change colour.

My uncles .... have two children.

4 Match each pair of <u>main clauses</u> on the board below. Then write them out as a <u>sentence</u> using a <u>conjunction</u>. Remember to put a <u>comma</u> in the correct place.

The sun is bright	I bought new boots
I went shopping	I have no map
I ask for directions	I put on suncream

for

and

so

....

....

....

"I can use commas correctly."

Section 9 — Brackets and Dashes

Brackets for Extra Information

Brackets are used to give extra information in a sentence.
You should always use two brackets in a sentence — never just one.

> Twinkle (the neighbour's rabbit) is hiding in my garden.

The extra information goes inside the brackets.
The sentence should still make sense without it.

1 Put a tick next to the sentences that use brackets correctly.

Our headteacher (Mr Bruce) cycles to school. ☐

(The weather) is lovely and sunny outside. ☐

Jenny (the girl who) lives next door plays the piano. ☐

I bought some pears (my favourite fruit) and plums. ☐

The plane (the biggest one I've ever seen) is taking off. ☐

My first lesson (maths with Miss Gater was) lots of fun. ☐

2 Each of these sentences only has one bracket.
Put the missing bracket in the correct box.

My little brother (a keen ☐ artist ☐ spilt some paint.

I added ☐ chillies to the meal ☐ a spicy curry).

He and his friend (who met ☐ last year ☐ play football together.

Jermaine studied two ☐ subjects ☐ English and French) at university.

Maximillian (Max to his ☐ friends ☐ was a successful businessman.

3 Add <u>brackets</u> in the <u>correct</u> positions in the sentences below.

Karl and Marie the bank robbers couldn't crack the safe .

I overtook the vehicle a caravan on the motorway .

Joan played the lead role a powerful superhero in the film .

Darcey beat her previous record 4 goals during the match .

4 Add <u>extra information</u> to each of these sentences by writing your own phrase in the <u>gaps</u> between the <u>brackets</u>.

The train (..............a rusty red one..............) pulled into the station.

Carrie's doll (...) is quite old.

The tickets (...) were expensive.

The caretaker (...) repaired the door.

5 Rewrite each of these sentences in the <u>correct order</u> using a <u>pair of brackets</u>.

| is eating grass | the cow | the brown one |

....

| a coffee | at the café | she bought a drink |

....

"I know how to use brackets in a sentence."

Section 9 — Brackets and Dashes

Dashes for Extra Information

A **pair of dashes** can also separate **extra information** in a sentence.

Cameron did the homework — a maths puzzle — very quickly.

Put the dashes around **the bits of extra information.**

1 Write the name of the person who uses <u>dashes correctly</u> in the space below.

Tomas   "I bought a chair — the last one broke from a shop — in town."

Devlin   "I took my car — it's nearly twenty years old — to the garage."

Amy   "I have — a snack an apple — every morning."

.... used dashes correctly.

2 In each of these sentences, there is one <u>dash</u> in an <u>incorrect</u> position. Cross it out and write a <u>new dash</u> in the correct position.

I went for a walk a — long one — in the woods.

We read — Macbeth a play by Shakespeare — in class.

Somebody for the — second time — had taken my mug.

3 Add a <u>pair of dashes</u> in the <u>correct</u> positions in the sentences below.

Oona a gymnast is training for a competition.

Mike pours a drink a glass of water from the jug.

Lions and wolves both excellent hunters live in groups.

Dylan kicked the football a new one into the stream.

4 Put a cross next to the sentence which has used <u>dashes</u> <u>incorrectly</u>. Then <u>rewrite</u> the sentence using dashes <u>correctly</u>.

Ted decided to call Li — when he wasn't driving — with the news. ☐

Han packed everything — except his toothbrush — for the trip. ☐

My dad built — with a bit of help a — treehouse last summer. ☐

Her last album — also award-winning — was excellent. ☐

....

....

5 <u>Rewrite</u> the sentence below in the <u>correct order</u> using a <u>pair of dashes</u>.

take a while to cook   tasty meals   especially stews

....

6 One <u>dash</u> in each sentence is in the <u>wrong</u> place.
Rewrite each sentence putting it in the <u>right</u> place.

The family two — parents and six children — are friendly.

....

The rocket — the red one — with the yellow stripes is flying into space.

....

We're going on holiday two weeks in Italy — in July —.

....

"I can use dashes to add extra information."   👍◯ 👎◯ 👎◯

Section 10 — Apostrophes

Apostrophes for Missing Letters

Apostrophes **show where** letters **have been left out** of a shortened **word.**

they are ⟹ they're   would have ⟹ would've

Sometimes the shortened word is quite different to the words it's made from.

will not ⟹ won't

1 **Circle the <u>correctly</u> shortened words.**

I will ⟹ Ill | I'll   they had ⟹ the'd | they'd

we have ⟹ we've | wev'e   can not ⟹ can't | cann't

he would ⟹ he'ld | he'd   who is ⟹ who's | wh'os

2 **Fill in the gaps below with the <u>complete</u> and <u>shortened</u> versions of the words.**

.........is not..........	isn't
do not	....
....	I've

let us	....
....	hasn't
should not	....

3 **Rewrite the sentence below using <u>shortened versions</u> of the underlined words.**

<u>They will</u> go if he <u>has not</u> lost the tickets.

....

"I can use apostrophes to shorten words."

Its and It's

The words 'its' and 'it's' look very similar, but they have **different meanings**.

| its | **This means 'belonging to it'.** ⟹ | the snake is in its tank |

| it's | **This means 'it is' or 'it has'.** ⟹ | it's wet | it's rained |

---

1 Draw lines to match each sentence with the **correct** meaning of '**its**' or '**it's**'.

 belonging to

 it is

 it has

It's green and fluffy.   It's been changed.   Its feet are huge.

---

2 Tick the sentences which use '**its**' or '**it's**' **correctly**.

It's ready to go. ☐   Its living under the floor. ☐

The kitten drank it's milk. ☐   They fixed its problems. ☐

It's a very tough job. ☐   The eel had a mind of it's own. ☐

---

3 Add <u>apostrophes</u> to the underlined words below, if they are <u>needed</u>.

The baby has an apple in <u>i t s</u> hand — <u>i t s</u> adorable!

<u>I t s</u> been a lovely day — <u>i t s</u> perfect weather for a BBQ.

I saw a monster — <u>i t s</u> teeth were huge and <u>i t s</u> skin was purple.

<u>I t s</u> important to look after your bag or <u>i t s</u> straps could break.

"I can use 'its' and 'it's' correctly."

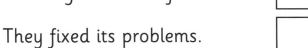

Apostrophes for Single Possession

You can show that someone or something owns something by adding an apostrophe and 's'. ——→ the builder's hammer

For singular nouns, always add the 's', even when the word already ends in 's'. ——→ the octopus's tentacle

1 Add an **apostrophe** to the underlined words to show single possession.

The <u>w a i t e r s</u> jacket was pink.　　The <u>w o m a n s</u> dinner was tasty.

A <u>b e e s</u> sting is painful.　　The <u>w a l r u s s</u> tusks are long.

2 Rewrite the underlined words with an **apostrophe** to show single possession.

Her <u>mums</u> car is parked outside.

....

The <u>coats</u> arms are too long.

....

The <u>donkeys</u> legs are stuck in the mud.

....

A <u>flamingos</u> feathers are pink or red.

....

3 Tick the **correct** version of each of these phrases to show single possession.

the zebra's stripes ☐　　the zebras' stripes ☐

the cheese's smell ☐　　the cheeses' smell ☐

the glass' design ☐　　the glass's design ☐

4 Complete these sentences by writing out the word in the box to show <u>single possession</u>.

shirt ⟹ The .... button has fallen off.

sister ⟹ My .... room is next to mine.

class ⟹ Our .... behaviour is good.

Gloria ⟹ .... shoes are orange and purple.

5 Complete the sentences to show <u>who</u> or <u>what</u> owns something.

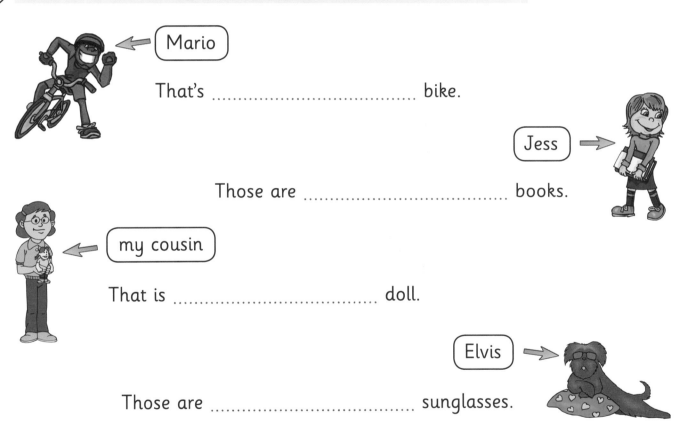

Mario

That's .... bike.

Jess

Those are .... books.

my cousin

That is .... doll.

Elvis

Those are .... sunglasses.

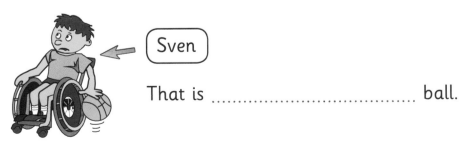

Sven

That is .... ball.

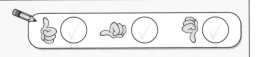

"I can use apostrophes to show single possession."

Section 10 — Apostrophes

Apostrophes for Plural Possession

You can use apostrophes to show possession for plural nouns.

the goats' kids

the children's toys

If a plural noun ends in 's', only add an apostrophe.

If a plural noun doesn't end in 's', add an apostrophe and an 's'.

1 Draw lines to match each word with the **correct** ending to show plural possession. Then write the completed words on the **board**.

bats

geese

women

elves

desks

nails

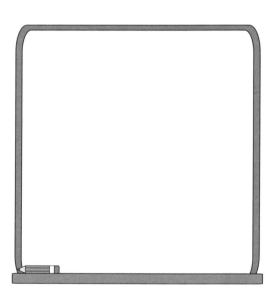

2 Circle the words which use **apostrophes** to show plural possession **correctly** to complete the sentences below.

We threw a surprise party for my <u>sisters'</u> / <u>sisters's</u> birthdays.

The light can be seen from the <u>houses's</u> / <u>houses'</u> windows.

The <u>curtains's</u> / <u>curtains'</u> patterns are quite old-fashioned.

<u>Mice's</u> / <u>Mices'</u> tails are usually shorter than rats' tails.

3 Write down what each group has using an apostrophe to show possession.

the players ➕ shirts ⟶ .... the players' shirts ....

the monkeys ➕ hands ⟶ ....

the men ➕ shoes ⟶ ....

the teachers ➕ meeting ⟶ ....

the people ➕ voices ⟶ ....

the dogs ➕ dinners ⟶ ....

4 Put a tick next to the sentences that use apostrophes for plural possession correctly and a cross next to the sentences that use them incorrectly.

The polar bears' home is in the Arctic. ☐

The children's faces lit up when they saw her. ☐

This bookshop sells the best authors's books. ☐

The horses' hooves are sore from running all day. ☐

The cakes's decorations look really pretty. ☐

None of the shirts' buttons are sewn on properly. ☐

Sharks' teeth are extremely sharp. ☐

Rewrite the incorrect sentences using apostrophes correctly.

....

....

"I can use apostrophes to show plural possession."

Apostrophe Practice

You can use apostrophes to show where letters are missing, or to show possession. Remember that 'its' and 'it's' are two different words.

1 **Tick the sentences that use apostrophes <u>correctly</u>.**

Jamie's dog hasn't ever barked at anyone. ☐

I should walk to the shops but it's going to rain. ☐

Colleen tripped over her trainers's laces. ☐

Matt is going out but he's forgotten his wallet. ☐

2 **Shorten these words using <u>apostrophes</u>.**

that is ⟹ ....   she will ⟹ ....

you would ⟹ ....   he had ⟹ ....

they are ⟹ ....   was not ⟹ ....

does not ⟹ ....   will not ⟹ ....

3 **Draw lines to match each <u>phrase</u> to its correct <u>meaning</u>.**

the boy's friends   one boy has one friend

the boys' friends   one boy has more than one friend

the boy's friend   two boys have one friend

the boys' friend   two boys have more than one friend

4 Draw lines to complete each sentence **correctly** with **its** or **it's**.

Shelley gave the cat .... food.

The guide dog led .... owner.

I can't use my car — .... broken.

The trampoline has lost .... bounce.

.... time for your piano lesson.

The squirrel buried .... nuts.

.... not a joke — this is serious.

its

it's

5 Write out these phrases to show single and plural **possession**. The **top** box contains **singular** nouns and the **bottom** box contains **plural** nouns.

church	+	window	→	the church's window
biker	+	helmet	→	....
giraffe	+	neck	→	....

carpenters	+	tools	→	....
waitresses	+	notepads	→	....
lizards	+	tongues	→	....

"I can use apostrophes correctly."

Section 10 — Apostrophes

Punctuating Speech

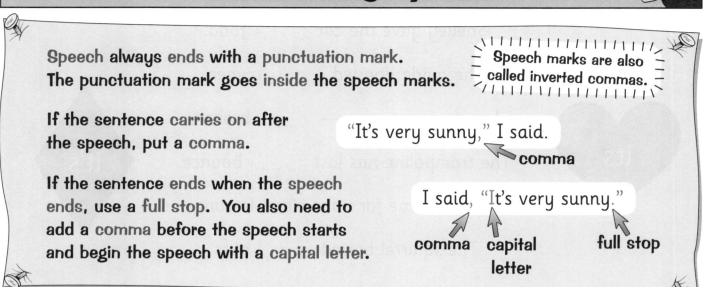

Speech **always** ends with a **punctuation mark**.
The punctuation mark goes **inside** the speech marks.

— Speech marks are also
— called inverted commas. —

If the sentence **carries on after**
the speech, put a **comma**.

"It's very sunny," I said.

← comma

If the sentence **ends** when the **speech**
ends, use a **full stop**. You also need to
add a **comma** before the speech starts
and begin the speech with a **capital letter**.

I said, "It's very sunny."

comma   capital   full stop
         letter

---

1 Put a <u>comma</u> or a <u>full stop</u> into the boxes to complete these sentences.

"Please tidy your room before dinner ⬚ " said Mum.

The judge announced, "The winner is Nadia ⬚ "

"I swept up the leaves ⬚ " she said.

Ibrahim explained ⬚ "I didn't eat your sandwich."

"He told me what you did," said the teacher ⬚

---

2 Put <u>inverted commas</u> (speech marks) in the <u>correct places</u> in the sentences below.

Can I look after your dog ? asked my friend .

We should work together on the project , said Polly .

Mr Lipton shouted , Get out of my garden !

The police officer asked , What did the thief look like ?

---

3 Tick the sentences which are <u>punctuated correctly</u>.

"We want to go to the aquarium" they said. ☐

She said, "Give the red sweets to Larry." ☐

"I need to visit the dentist soon," said Shona. ☐

"Dhara shouted, What enormous shoes you have!" ☐

4 Put the <u>punctuation</u> in the boxes into each of the sentences. They are in the order that they will appear in the sentence.

(,) (") (.) (")   Sophie said Netball is my favourite sport

(") (?) (") (.)   What time does it start asked Liam

(") (!) (") (.)   How exhausted I am he exclaimed

(") (,) (") (.)   You should eat more fruit said the doctor

5 Put the <u>correct punctuation marks</u> into the boxes to complete the sentences.

☐ I will help you build a sandcastle ☐ " said Mia.

"Take the dog for a walk, ☐ said Dad ☐

☐ Can we plant some flowers ☐ " asked my little brother.

Johan shouted ☐ "Show me where you've hidden the toys ☐ "

"I can punctuate speech with full stops and commas." 👍 ✓ 🤙 ✓ 👎 ✓

Direct and Reported Speech

You only use speech marks if you're writing down exactly what someone has said. This is called direct speech.

"I found a shell," said Chetna. This is direct speech — it's exactly what Chetna has said.

If you're just talking about what someone has said, you don't need speech marks. This is called reported speech.

Chetna said that she found a shell. This is reported speech — it's just reporting what Chetna said.

1 Draw lines to show whether each of these sentences is <u>direct speech</u> or <u>reported speech</u>.

"I can't tell you because it's a secret," he said.

Lynn said you should ask him.

"Listen to me!" yelled Kyle.

They told us you went to London.

Benaiah asked, "What is that smell?"

2 Draw lines to match the <u>direct speech</u> on the left with the <u>reported speech</u> on the right.

"I'm very thirsty," said Kirsty.

We said we couldn't go today.

We said, "We can't go today."

Zack shouted for us to come back.

Zack shouted, "Come back!"

Kirsty said she was thirsty.

3 **Tick the sentences which need <u>inverted commas</u>.**

The children told the teacher what happened. ☐

I can't find my gloves, said Ameera. ☐

Vinny said, This level is easier than the first one. ☐

I heard her say she didn't want to go. ☐

Lauren said everyone had worked very hard. ☐

My name is Feathers, said the parrot. ☐

4 **Write the sentences on the correct <u>board</u> to show whether they are <u>direct speech</u> or <u>reported speech</u>.**

<u>Direct speech</u>

<u>Reported speech</u>

He said he hates cats.

"Why are you upset?"

"Let's buy them a gift."

We told them to behave.

"Get out of my way!"

I said I needed help.

"I can use direct and reported speech."

Paragraphs

Paragraphs group sentences together around the same theme.

Start a new paragraph for a new time, place or subject, and when someone new speaks. You show a new paragraph by starting a new line and leaving a space.

1 Tick the correct reasons for starting a new paragraph.

You want to write about a new place. ☐

You've run out of space on the page. ☐

Someone new is going to speak. ☐

You want to write about a different topic. ☐

You want to have space for a picture. ☐

You want to write about a different time. ☐

2 Draw lines to match the sentences that belong in the same paragraph.

Sailing is a fun and relaxing hobby for people who like the sea.	Yesterday broke the record for the hottest day of the year.
Halim likes to watch sport on the television.	You can compete in races or sail to distant places.
The weather has been unusually warm this summer.	He loves football because he enjoys the commentary.

(3) Use <u>paragraph markers</u> (//) to break this passage into <u>four paragraphs</u>.

Today, my class worked outside because the weather was so nice. We drew pictures of the flowers in the school field. I drew a daffodil. When we were done, Mr Davies told us to go to the pond. "How exciting!" said my friend Martha, "I've never been there before." At the pond, we looked for frogs and newts.

Give a <u>reason</u> for starting each <u>new paragraph</u>.

2nd paragraph ....

3rd paragraph ....

4th paragraph ....

(4) Write a sentence that could go in the <u>same paragraph</u> as the sentences below.

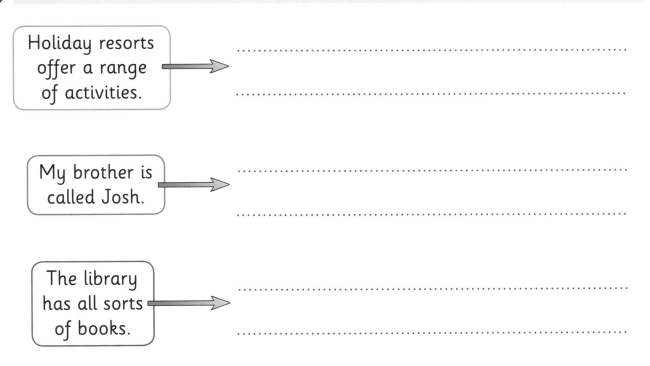

Holiday resorts offer a range of activities.

....

....

My brother is called Josh.

....

....

The library has all sorts of books.

....

....

"I can organise a piece of writing into paragraphs."

Section 12 — Paragraphs and Layout

Headings and Subheadings

Headings and subheadings make a text clearer and easier to read.

Headings tell the reader the main topic of the text.

Subheadings divide up the text into smaller sections and help to put information in a logical order.

1 Label the headings and subheadings in the text below.

.... →

.... →

.... →

.... →

> **CLARA'S CAKE COMPANY**
>
> <u>All sizes, shapes and flavours</u>
>
> Our speciality is strawberry cupcakes, but we'll make anything you want to eat.
>
> <u>Free delivery</u>
>
> We'll deliver free to any event in the local area.
>
> <u>Contact us!</u>
>
> Give us a call or send us an email!

2 Draw lines to link each subheading to the correct section of the text.

September	October	December

Have a spooky costume ready, as Halloween is just around the corner...

It's almost time for the Christmas holidays and the Nativity play is ready to go...

School starts now, so all our pupils will be excited to meet their new teachers...

"I understand how to use headings and subheadings."

Prefixes — 're' 'anti' and 'auto'

A prefix is a letter or group of letters that can be added to the beginning of a word (called a root word) to make a new word.

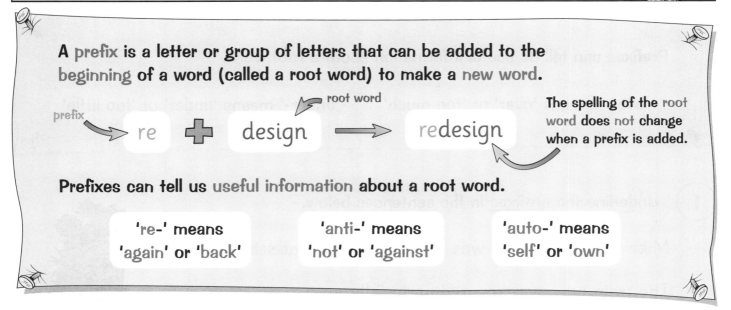

prefix

root word

re ➕ design ⟶ redesign

The spelling of the root word does not change when a prefix is added.

Prefixes can tell us useful information about a root word.

| 're-' means 'again' or 'back' | 'anti-' means 'not' or 'against' | 'auto-' means 'self' or 'own' |

1 Draw lines to match each word to the <u>correct</u> prefix. Then write the new words on the <u>board</u>.

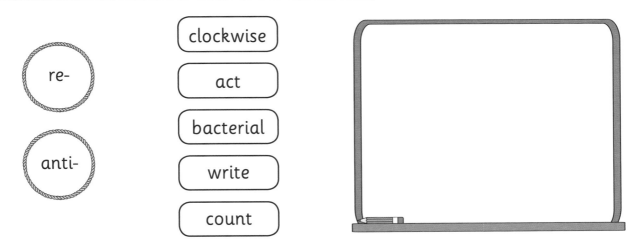

re-

anti-

clockwise

act

bacterial

write

count

2 Complete the words in these sentences using <u>re-</u>, <u>anti-</u> or <u>auto-</u>.

The actress has just written an .... biography about her life.

The ghost .... appeared on the other side of the wall.

When I fell over, my mum put .... septic cream on my grazes.

Marc asked for the tennis player's .... graph after the game.

Prefixes — 'under' 'over' 'en' and 'em'

Prefixes can tell us **useful information** about a root word.

'over-' means 'over' or 'too much'   'under-' means 'under' or 'too little'

1 **Underline the prefixes in the sentences below.**

Mike worried that he was underperforming at school.

The train was overcrowded and really noisy.

The garden of the abandoned house was really overgrown.

2 **Tick the sentences where the underlined word has the correct prefix.**

My brother won't <u>overeat</u> because he hates feeling too full.

She is much too sure she will win — she is <u>underconfident</u>.

Manuel wears baggy and <u>undersized</u> clothes.

Jamal baked his cake for too long so it was <u>overcooked</u>.

3 **Use the clues to work out each word beginning with under- or over-.**

not paid enough ⟹ | | | | | p | | i | d |

| | | | | l | o | | d | ⟸ put too much on

not valued enough ⟹ | | | | | | r | a | t | | d |

'En' and 'em' are common prefixes.

'Em' is used instead of 'en' when the root word starts with a 'b' or 'p'.

'en' is the prefix ⟹ enforce   embitter ⟸ 'bitter' is a root word which starts with 'b'

(4) **Complete the words in these sentences using en- or em-.**

I want to ....large this photograph to hang on the wall.

Luci tried to be quiet so she didn't ....rage the teacher.

Niall couldn't escape the ....brace of Great Aunt Maggie.

I'd like to set a good example and ....courage others.

The couple are about to ....bark on a journey together.

(5) **Choose the word with the correct prefix in each pair and write it in the box.**

emclose / enclose

enchant / emchant

enpower / empower

....
....
....

Then use the words you wrote in the box to complete these sentences.

A wicked wizard tried to .... the princess.

I hope the speech will .... people.

They are planning to .... the field with a fence.

Prefixes — 'mid' 'pre' 'fore' and 'non'

Prefixes can give us useful information about a root word.

'mid-' means 'middle'.   'pre-' and 'fore-' mean 'before'.   'non-' means 'not'.

| mid**day** | pre**heat** | fore**cast** | non**living** |

1 Draw lines to match each word to the **correct** prefix.
Then write the completed words in the box.

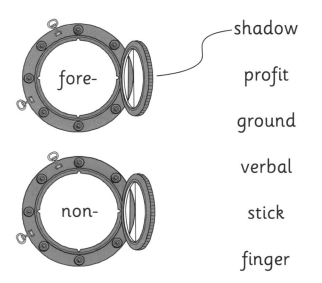

fore-

non-

shadow

profit

ground

verbal

stick

finger

foreshadow

2 Circle the **correct** spelling of each word to complete the sentences below.

The weather is really hot in <u>presummer</u> / <u>midsummer</u>.

We had to <u>preselect</u> / <u>midselect</u> what we wanted for lunch.

She is the best <u>midfielder</u> / <u>prefielder</u> in the team.

We're learning about <u>prehistoric</u> / <u>midhistoric</u> creatures in class.

After 3 days, I reached the <u>prepoint</u> / <u>midpoint</u> of my 6-day holiday.

3 Choose <u>mid-</u>, <u>pre-</u>, <u>fore-</u> or <u>non-</u> to add to each root word below. Then write the completed word in the <u>correct</u> puzzle piece.

stop   night   air   arrange   see   sense   head   pay

<u>mid-</u>

<u>pre-</u>

<u>fore-</u>

<u>non-</u>

4 Use the clues to work out the words starting with <u>mid-</u>, <u>pre-</u>, <u>fore-</u> or <u>non-</u>.

to alert in advance ➡️ | | | | | w | | r | n |

to see in advance ➡️ | | | | v | i | | w |

5 Rewrite these sentences, adding the <u>correct</u> prefix from the boxes below to the underlined words. Use each prefix only <u>once</u>.

pre-   mid-

The baby was born early — it was <u>mature</u>.

....

Every day, I have a <u>morning</u> cup of tea.

....

Word Endings — the 'shun' sound

The 'shun' sound at the end of words can be spelt in **different** ways.

'-tion' is used when the root word ends in **'t'** or **'te'**.   direct ⟹ direction

'-cian' is used when the root word ends in **'c'** or **'cs'**.   magic ⟹ magician

---

(1) Unscramble the letters in the boxes to make words ending in the '**shun**' sound.

'-cian' is often used for occupations.

l & i c	n i a	i l o p	p t a
i a t c	c u	a i c	n & i
r e n	s m i	i n t	c i

e........................   m........................   p........................   o........................

---

(2) Add in the **missing 'c' or 't'** to these words ending with a '**shun**' sound.

 c    t

ac..........ion   invita..........ion   posi..........ion

fic..........ion   mathemati..........ian   techni..........ian

men..........ion   conversa..........ion   hesita..........ion

---

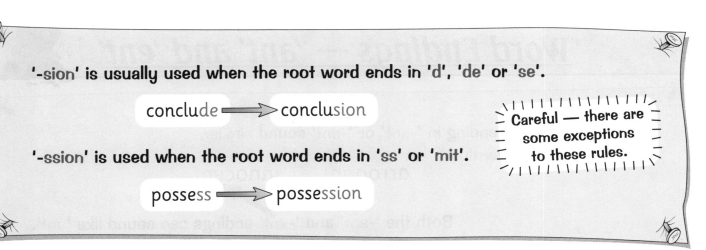

'-sion' is usually used when the root word ends in 'd', 'de' or 'se'.

conclude ⟹ conclusion

'-ssion' is used when the root word ends in 'ss' or 'mit'.

possess ⟹ possession

Careful — there are some exceptions to these rules.

3 Circle the **correct spelling** of these '**shun**' sound words.

I watched the colourful carnival <u>procesion</u> / <u>procession</u> go past.

After school, we watched cartoons on the <u>television</u> / <u>televission</u>.

When the volcano erupted, there was a huge <u>explosion</u> / <u>explossion</u>.

My parents gave me <u>permision</u> / <u>permission</u> to go on the school trip.

Elliot and I had never heard that <u>verssion</u> / <u>version</u> of the song.

4 Draw lines to match each <u>ending</u> to the correct <u>root word</u>, then write the <u>new word</u> on the line. The first one has been done for you.

tion

sion

ssion

accommodate ⟹ accommodation ....

collide ⟹ ....

extend ⟹ ....

relate ⟹ ....

confuse ⟹ ....

discuss ⟹ ....

admit ⟹ ....

Section 14 — Word Endings and Suffixes

Word Endings — 'ant' and 'ent'

Sometimes words ending in '-ant' or '-ent' sound similar, but are spelt differently.

arrog**ant**   innoc**ent**

Both the '-ant' and '-ent' endings can sound like 'unt'.

1 Draw a line to connect the start of each word to its correct **word ending**.

expect-

independ-

reluct-

abs-

ant

ent

contest-

incid-

intellig-

instrum-

2 Put a cross next to the **four** words that are **spelt incorrectly**. Write the **correct spellings** on the board below.

confident ☐   patiant ☐   urgant ☐   violent ☐

important ☐   different ☐   brillient ☐   elegant ☐

3 Use the clues to work out each word ending in '-**ant**' or '-**ent**'.

another word for a 'gift' ⟹ | p | | e | | | n | |

another word for 'very quiet' ⟹ | s | i | | | | t |

another word for 'far away' ⟹ | d | | s | t | | | t |

another word for 'really old' ⟹ | a | n | | i | | n | |

a butler or maid ⟹ | s | | r | v | | | t |

4 Circle the <u>correct spelling</u> of the underlined words.

The teacher wrote on the board in <u>permanent</u> / <u>permanant</u> marker.

Kian told some really funny jokes in his <u>recant</u> / <u>recent</u> show.

France is part of the European <u>continent</u> / <u>continant</u>.

Thea thought the summer picnic was very <u>pleasant</u> / <u>pleasent</u>.

The magician's stage name was Marco the <u>Magnificent</u> / <u>Magnificant</u>.

It is <u>conveniant</u> /<u>convenient</u> to have a shop around the corner.

5 Rewrite the sentence with the <u>underlined words</u> spelt correctly.

The <u>disobediant</u> <u>elephent</u> escaped from the zoo.

....

....

Section 14 — Word Endings and Suffixes

Word Endings — 'ance', 'ancy' and 'ence', 'ency'

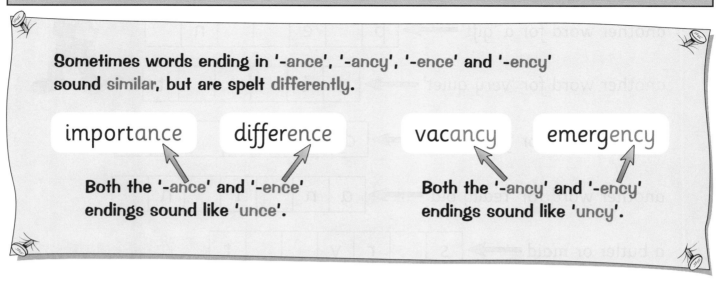

Sometimes words ending in '-ance', '-ancy', '-ence' and '-ency' sound similar, but are spelt differently.

| importance | difference | vacancy | emergency |

Both the '-ance' and '-ence' endings sound like 'unce'.

Both the '-ancy' and '-ency' endings sound like 'uncy'.

1 Draw lines to show whether each word is spelt **correctly** or **incorrectly**.

sciance

instance

absence

patiance

Correct spelling

Incorrect spelling

obedience

ignorence

innocance

balance

2 Complete each of the words below with the correct **ending**.

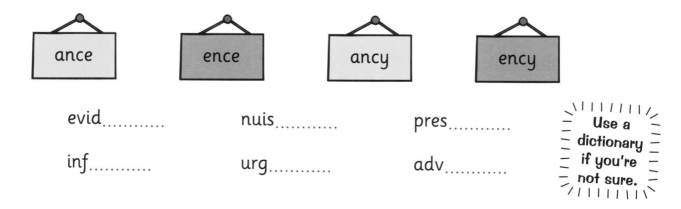

| ance | ence | ancy | ency |

evid............   nuis............   pres............

inf............   urg............   adv............

Use a dictionary if you're not sure.

3 Circle the __correct spelling__ of the underlined words.

The band gave an incredible __performence__ / __performance__.

People who act with __decency__ / __decancy__ make good friends.

Henry called an ambulance because it was an __emergancy__ / __emergency__.

I don't have much __experience__ / __experiance__ of looking after pets.

A __pregnancy__ / __pregnency__ usually lasts about nine months.

4 Solve the clues to complete the __crossword__.

Clues
1. people who watch a show
2. another word for advice
3. another word for money
4. the opposite of shyness
5. an opening, e.g. for a job
6. where you enter a building

A thesaurus might help you here.

Word Endings — 'able', 'ible', 'ably' and 'ibly'

Words ending in '-able' and '-ible' can sound similar, but are spelt differently.

reliable   horrible

Words ending in '-ably' and '-ibly' can sound similar too. They can also be spelt differently.

adorably   incredibly

1 Match the beginnings of the words to their <u>correct endings</u>.

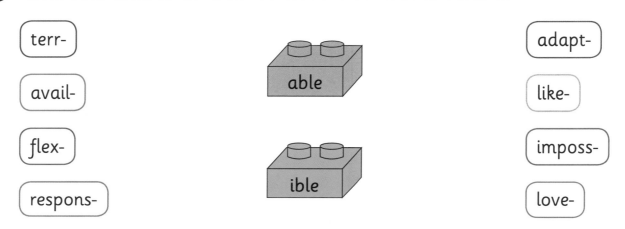

terr-
avail-
flex-
respons-

able

ible

adapt-
like-
imposs-
love-

2 Sort the letters below into the right order to spell a <u>root word</u>. Add '<u>-able</u>' and '<u>-ably</u>' or '<u>-ible</u>' and '<u>-ibly</u>' to each root word to make <u>two new words</u>.

root word   new words

e n
s a k
o

r.................................   ....

....

a c
e c s
s

a.................................   ....

....

3 Underline the <u>correct spelling</u> of each word.

excitibly　excitably

fashionibly　fashionably

invisably　invisibly

respectably　respectibly

sensibly　sensably

possibly　possably

4 Circle the <u>correct spelling</u> of the underlined words ending with <u>-able</u> or <u>-ible</u>.

My parents' new sofa was very <u>comfortable</u> / <u>comfortible</u>.

I found a <u>suitible</u> / <u>suitable</u> dress for the party in the sale.

The weather is absolutely <u>horrable</u> / <u>horrible</u> today.

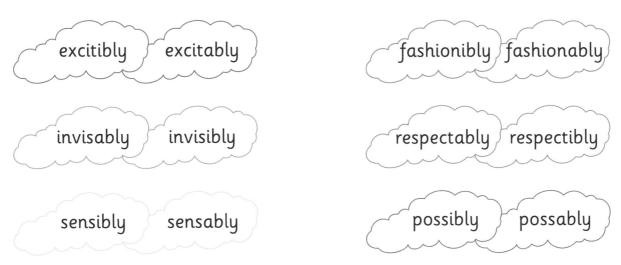

Simone took a <u>sizeible</u> / <u>sizeable</u> piece of chocolate cake.

He said he could cook, but his food was barely <u>edible</u> / <u>edable</u>.

5 Complete the words in these sentences using <u>-ably</u> or <u>-ibly</u>.

The schoolchildren were impecc........................ dressed in their uniforms.

Niamh's mum was justifi........................ angry that she hadn't tidied up.

Martyn was incred........................ upset after hearing the news.

A thick layer of snow is vis........................ settling on the ground.

Our class did remark........................ well in sports day this year.

Suffixes

A **suffix** is a letter or group of letters that can be **added** to the end of a **root word** to make a **new word**.

'sad' is the root word. → **sad** ➕ **ly** → **sadly** ← '-ly' is a suffix.

Sometimes the **spelling** of the root word **changes** when a suffix is added.

angry ➕ **ly** → **angrily** ← The 'y' in 'angry' changes to 'i' when the suffix '-ly' is added.

---

1 Add '**-ly**' or '**-ous**' to the word beginnings below.

weird..........   vari..........   hazard..........

fam..........   bare..........   right..........

timid..........   gorge..........   live..........

enorm..........   love..........   humor..........

---

2 Draw lines to connect these words to the correct <u>suffixes</u>.

real   organ

final   **-ify**   custom

class   just

solid   **-ise**   advert

familiar   test

---

3 Circle the <u>correct spelling</u> of the underlined words.

During the holidays, we are going to <u>decorate</u> / <u>decorify</u> my bedroom.

Arlo must <u>specificise</u> / <u>specify</u> which route he wants us to take.

Spenser and Seren are going to <u>revisate</u> / <u>revise</u> for the spelling test.

I can't hear my phone <u>vibrate</u> / <u>vibrise</u> when it's in my pocket.

The hotel can <u>accommodise</u> / <u>accommodate</u> up to 70 people.

I will <u>summarate</u> / <u>summarise</u> the plot of the book for you.

4 Tick the root words that will <u>change</u> when the <u>suffix '-ly'</u> is added.

happy ☐   poor ☐   day ☐
odd ☐   scary ☐   quiet ☐

Write out the words you have ticked with the <u>suffix</u> attached.

....

5 Add '<u>-ous</u>' or '<u>-ate</u>' to the <u>root words</u> below.
Then write the <u>new words</u> out in full.

danger ✚ .... ➡ ....

origin ✚ .... ➡ ....

joy ✚ .... ➡ ....

moment ✚ .... ➡ ....

passion ✚ .... ➡ ....

Section 14 — Word Endings and Suffixes

'ei' and 'ie' Words

Use this rhyme to help you remember how to spell ei and ie words:

'i' before 'e' except after 'c' if the vowel sound rhymes with bee

brief ← Rhymes with bee, so 'i' before 'e'.

receive ← Rhymes with bee, but follows a 'c' — so 'e' before 'i'.

height ← Doesn't rhyme with bee, so 'e' before 'i'.

efficient ← Doesn't rhyme with bee and follows a 'c' — so 'i' before 'e'.

---

①   Add <u>ei</u> or <u>ie</u> to each word below. Then draw lines to match it to its picture.

w.........ght   sc.........ntist   p.........ce   ch.........f

---

②   Complete the words below using either <u>ei</u> or <u>ie</u>.

Marie was determined to ach.........ve all her goals.

She felt a huge sense of rel.........f when her test was over.

Jack couldn't bel.........ve what he had seen.

Sophie likes to go on holiday to for.........gn countries.

I flipped my pancake too high and it stuck to the c.........ling.

Some words don't follow the 'i before e' rule — you just have to learn these.

caffeine

3 Circle the **correct** spelling in each pair of words.

> All the words in the box are exception words.

seize / sieze   speceis / species

protien / protein   friend / freind

Then use the **correct** versions of each word to complete these sentences.

.... is an important part of a balanced diet.

Annika is going on holiday with her best ....

The police are going to .... the criminal's stolen goods.

They have discovered a new .... of shark.

4 Solve the **clues** to complete the crossword.

> All the words are 'ei' or 'ie' words.

Across

1. Playful trouble

2. A big area of grass

3. Someone who steals

Down

1. Very old

2. A record of what you bought

3. Odd or bizarre

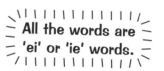

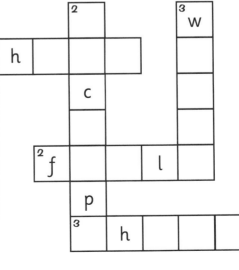

Section 15 — Confusing Words

Words with 'ough' in

Words that contain the letters 'ough' can sound very different.

trough	though	tough

Here, the 'ough' sounds like 'off'.

Here, the 'ough' sounds like 'oh'.

Here, the 'ough' sounds like 'uff'.

1 Read these sentences then write the name of the person who pronounces the 'ough' sound correctly.

Seamus — "The 'ough' sound in 'enough' sounds like 'off'."

Hani — "The 'ough' sound in 'although' sounds like 'oh'."

Isabella — "The 'ough' sound in 'cough' sounds like 'uff'."

.... pronounces the 'ough' sound correctly.

2 Unscramble the words in the coloured boxes. Use the definitions to help you. Each word contains 'ough'.

The first and last letters are in the correct places.

t g u o h	....	difficult
r u g o l h y	....	not smoothly
d h u o u n g t	....	a sugary, jam-filled cake
c u g o h	....	you do this to clear your throat
t u r g o h	....	an animal's food container

plough ← Here, the 'ough' sounds like 'ow'.

borough ← Here, the 'ough' sounds like 'uh'.

fought ← Here, the 'ough' sounds like 'or'.

through ← Here, the 'ough' sounds like 'oo'.

(3) Draw lines to match each <u>ough</u> word with the correct sound.

thought

sought

'or'

drought

bough

'ow'

ought

thoughtful

(4) Sort the words below into pairs that <u>rhyme</u>.

plough   bought   bough   nought

thorough   borough

....

....

(5) Use the clues to work out each word containing <u>ough</u>.

past tense of bring ⟹ [ ][r][ ][ ][ ][t]

an idea ⟹ [t][h][ ][ ][ ][ ][ ]

a lack of water ⟹ [d][ ][ ][ ][ ][t]

in one side and out of the other side ⟹ [t][ ][r][ ][ ][ ][ ]

Words with Silent Letters

Silent letters are letters you don't hear when you say a word.

knife   wrap   crumb   The 'k', 'w' and 'b' are the silent letters in these words.

1 Circle the silent letters in each of the words below.

k n i c k e r s   w r e c k   t h u m b

a n s w e r   d u m b   h o n e s t

2 Draw lines to match each incomplete word with its missing silent letter. Then, write the completed words in the box.

.....nee   w

lam.....   k

.....rist   h

g.....ost   b

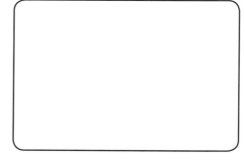

3 Fill in the silent letters in these words so that they match the pictures.

cas.....le   plum.....er   .....nuckle   s.....ord

4 Draw lines to show what the <u>silent letter</u> is in each word below.

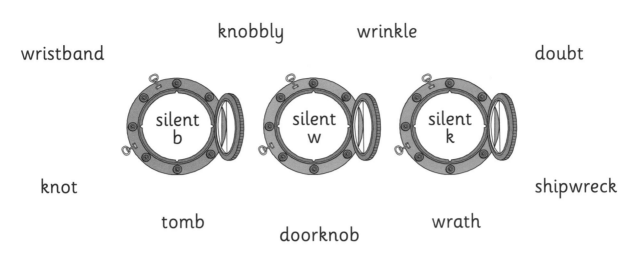

knobbly   wrinkle

wristband   doubt

silent b   silent w   silent k

knot   shipwreck

tomb   doorknob   wrath

5 Use the picture clues to <u>work out</u> what each word is. Write the words in the boxes.

Each word contains a silent letter.

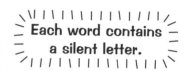

		s	c		t	s

		i		h	

		i	s			r	s

6 Circle the <u>correct</u> spelling in each pair of words.

wrestle / restle   clyme / climb   wisthle / whistle

Then use the <u>correct spelling</u> of each word to complete these sentences.

Maya is going to .... Mount Everest this summer.

The referee blew his .... at the end of the game.

My sisters used to .... each other in the hall.

Homophones

Homophones are words that are pronounced the same, but have different meanings and spellings.

son ⟸ A son is a male child.

sun ⟸ The sun is what you can see in the sky during the day.

1 Unscramble the **letters** to complete the **words**. Use the pictures to help you.

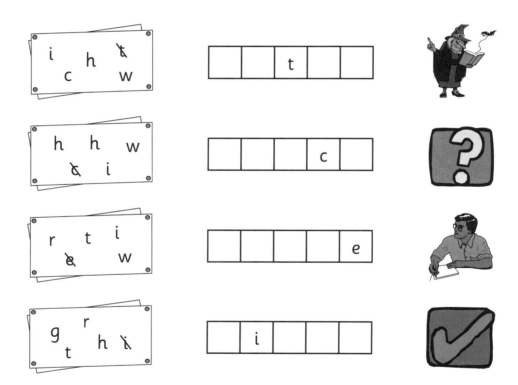

| | | t | | |

| | | | c | |

| | | | | e |

| | i | | | |

2 Find **homophones** for the words below.

weak ⟹ | w | | | k |

bawl ⟹ | b | | | l |

new ⟹ | k | | | w |

meddle ⟹ | m | | | l |

grate ⟹ | g | | | t |

flower ⟹ | f | | | r |

3 Draw lines to match each word to its <u>meaning</u>.

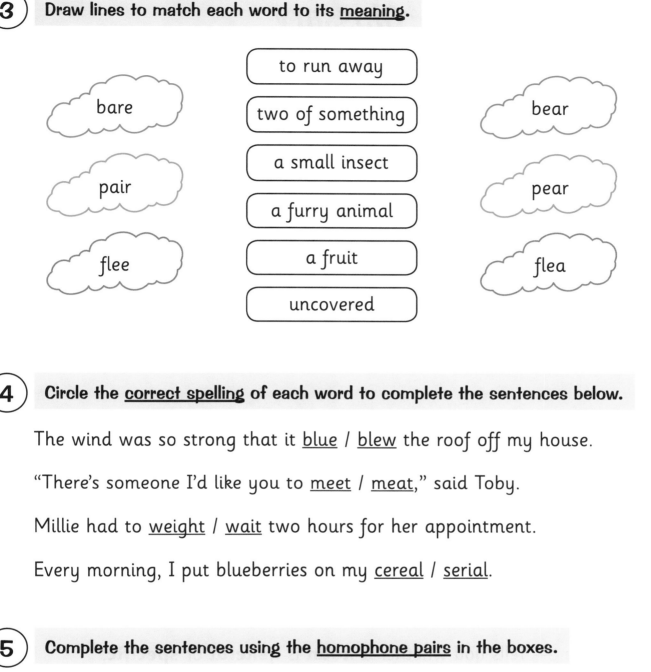

bare

pair

flee

to run away

two of something

a small insect

a furry animal

a fruit

uncovered

bear

pear

flea

4 Circle the <u>correct spelling</u> of each word to complete the sentences below.

The wind was so strong that it <u>blue</u> / <u>blew</u> the roof off my house.

"There's someone I'd like you to <u>meet</u> / <u>meat</u>," said Toby.

Millie had to <u>weight</u> / <u>wait</u> two hours for her appointment.

Every morning, I put blueberries on my <u>cereal</u> / <u>serial</u>.

5 Complete the sentences using the <u>homophone pairs</u> in the boxes.

road / rode

Mhairi .... her bike down the ....

board / bored

We were .... so we played a .... game.

sail / sale

Marcus saw a boat's .... for ....

Glossary

Adjective — A word that describes a noun, e.g. **huge** whale, **smelly** sock.

Adverb — A word that describes a **verb**, an **adjective** or other **adverbs**. e.g. **quickly**, **possibly**, **soon**.

Adverbial — A group of words that behaves like an **adverb**.

Article — The words '**a**', '**an**' and '**the**'. They are used to make a **noun** either **general** or **specific**.

Clause — Part of a sentence that contains a **subject** and a **verb**.

Cohesion — **Linking** ideas together to make your writing **flow smoothly**.

Conjunction — A word or phrase that **joins** two parts of a sentence. e.g. We like chocolate <u>and</u> we like toffee.

Determiner — Tells you whether a **noun** is **general** or **specific**. e.g. I bought <u>an</u> orange. I bought <u>this</u> orange.

Exclamation — A sentence that shows **strong emotion**, beginning with 'how' or 'what'.

Main clause — A clause that **makes sense** on its own. e.g. <u>He swept the floor</u> before they arrived.

Noun — A word that **names** something, e.g. **October**, **train**, **Morgan**.

Glossary

Parenthesis — A part of a sentence that gives **extra information**.

Phrase — A group of words usually without a **verb**, e.g. by the water, the warm woollen jumper with red and blue stripes.

Possessive pronoun — A word that shows **who owns** something, e.g. **his**, **mine**, **yours**.

Preposition — Tells you **where**, **when**, or **why** something happens. e.g. The birds flew <u>under</u> the bridge.

Pronoun — A word used to **replace** a **noun**, e.g. **me**, **she**, **you**.

Relative clause — A **subordinate clause** that tells you more about a noun. It's often introduced by a relative pronoun, e.g. That's the bag **<u>which</u>** <u>is broken</u>.

Relative pronoun — A word that connects a **relative clause** to a **main clause**, e.g. There's the cake <u>which</u> I wanted.

Standard English — The formal type of language you use in written work.

Subordinate clause — A clause that **doesn't make sense** on its **own** and usually **begins** with a **subordinating conjunction**. e.g. I went to bed **<u>because</u>** <u>I was tired</u>.

Verb — A doing or being word, e.g. **run**, **draw**, **climb**, **are**.

Glossary

COMMON PUNCTUATION MARKS

Apostrophes — show **missing letters** and **possession**. `'`

Brackets — **separate extra information** in a sentence. They can also be called **parentheses**. `( )`

Capital letters — used for **starting** sentences and for **names** or **I**. `A`

Commas — used in **lists**, to **join clauses**, to separate **extra information** and after some **introductions** (**adverbial phrases**). `,`

Dashes — separate **extra information** in a sentence. `–`

Exclamation marks — show **strong emotions** or **commands**. `!`

Full stops — show where **sentences end**. `.`

Inverted commas — show **direct speech**. `" "`

Question marks — used at the **end** of **questions**. `?`

Answers

Grammar

Section 1 — Word Types

Page 4 — Nouns

1. Concrete nouns: **mountain, custard, paperclip, school, computer**
   Abstract nouns: **fear, joy, generosity, kindness, delight**

2. You should have ticked these phrases: a herd of cows, the class of children, a pack of wolves

Page 5 — Adjectives

1. You should have connected these adjectives to the puzzle piece: **grumpy, helpful, disgusting, interesting, rough, dangerous**

2. The gardener cut back the **spiky** rose bush.
   Leon put his **filthy** football kit in the laundry basket.

3. Any suitable adjectives to replace good and bad.
   Examples:
   The rides at the theme park were **exciting**. Overall, I had a **fantastic** day.
   I don't like aeroplanes — flying is **terrifying** and the food tastes **disgusting**.

Page 6 — Verbs

1. Maya <u>makes</u> models out of clay.
   The hamster always <u>hides</u> behind the sofa.
   That book <u>has</u> a very happy ending.
   My uncle <u>is</u> a policeman in London.
   On Tuesdays, Jacob <u>takes</u> the bus home.
   You <u>are</u> much taller than my brother.

2. Harry **rides** his bike.
   We **live** in Bristol.
   Evan **enjoys** school.
   You **read** short stories.
   My best friend **is** from Spain.
   I **do** karate on Mondays.
   They **cook** pizza.
   Felix **has** three cats.

Pages 7-9 — Adverbs

1. My large, brown, bulky parcel **finally** arrived.
   Remi and Tomas **usually** eat their lunch in the hall.
   Mum says it is **extremely** difficult to become a lawyer.
   The magician **suddenly** turned into a frog!
   My brother plays a **really** nice guitar.

2. Rania **gently** took her hamster out of its cage.
   We arrived at the airport **very** early.
   The police officer looked **sternly** at the thief.
   The gymnast performed his routine **perfectly**.
   Yusef doesn't have a watch, so he's **usually** late.

3. Certain: **definitely, certainly, surely**
   Not certain: **maybe, perhaps, possibly**

4. You should have ticked these sentences:
   Jared will <u>definitely</u> have a bigger portion than I will.
   My friends are <u>certainly</u> enjoying the party.
   You should have crossed these sentences:
   <u>Perhaps</u> I'll go for a walk in the woods.
   <u>Maybe</u> the teacher will forget about our test.
   Humans will <u>possibly</u> live on Mars one day.

5. I haven't seen Felix, but he's **probably** in the garden.
   If you want to pass your exams, you must **certainly** study.
   Maybe we could go to the beach tomorrow.

6. She is **certainly** going to win a gold medal.
   Finn is **definitely** going to be a nurse.
   Surely they won't be late.
   That is **undoubtedly** a good book.

7. Any suitable adverbs that make the two sentences sound more then less certain.
   Examples:
   We are **definitely** going to Greece in the summer.
   We are **maybe** going to Greece in the summer.
   Fatima will **certainly** play football this weekend.
   Fatima will **possibly** play football this weekend.

Pages 10 and 11 — Pronouns

1. Noah asked Verity if <u>she</u> wanted to play outside with <u>him</u>.
   <u>They</u> stole our garden gnome and replaced <u>it</u> with a muddy boot.
   <u>We</u> didn't go to the party because <u>it</u> started too late.
   Bianca brought sweets for the class and shared <u>them</u> between <u>us</u>.
   The postman delivers the post, but sometimes <u>he</u> brings <u>it</u> very late.

2. Khalid got mud on Saul's trouser, so he washed <u>the trousers</u> for <u>Saul</u>. — **them, him**
   Stacey built a treehouse for Amy, then took <u>Amy</u> to play in the <u>treehouse</u>. — **her, it**
   Paco and Julia found a secret cave, so <u>Paco and Julia</u> explored <u>the cave</u>. — **they, it**

3. Mr Chang is a good teacher. **He** makes our lessons really fun.
   My brother and I are shopping. **We** are buying a gift for our mum.
   Dean and Samantha are mischievous. **They** always get in trouble.
   My best friend has a new baby sister. I can't wait to meet **her**.
   Karl, my pen pal, lives in Germany. I write to **him** once a week.
   Annie borrowed my favourite jumper. I hope **she** gives **it** back.

4. Nicky and Shane are in a band. **They are really talented.**
   Emilia really enjoyed the film. **She wants to watch it again.**

Pages 12 and 13 — Possessive Pronouns

1. You should have connected these possessive pronouns to the hook: **theirs, mine, yours, his, ours, hers**

2. My friend's dog is much smaller than **mine**.
   I forgot my pens. Can I borrow **yours**?
   Maria's car had broken down, so we took **ours**.
   Aziz accidentally burst Priya's football, so he gave her **his**.

3. The cat belongs to Mina. The cat is **hers**.
   They bought a new sofa. The sofa is **theirs**.
   I made a poster in school. The poster is **mine**.
   Safiya returned Ben's pen after school, because it was **his**.
   Someone else sat in seats 8 and 9, although they were **ours**.

Answers

4. The ice-cream is **theirs**.
   The mug is **hers**.
   The chess set is **theirs**.
   The helmet is **his**.

Page 14 — Relative Pronouns

1. I met a sailor **who** has sailed on every ocean.
   She's going to the shop **which** sells motorbikes.
   They always go to places **which** are warm and sunny.
   Rafael is the person **who** painted my room.

2. My next door neighbour is the man **who** owns the bakery.
   We used to have a cat **which** only had three legs.
   That's the lady **whose** daughter is a scientist.
   I like books **which** are full of adventure.

Pages 15 and 16 — Articles and Determiners

1. I have <u>a</u> pet moose called Jared.
   <u>The</u> bell rang, so we took <u>a</u> break.
   All <u>the</u> teachers and <u>the</u> pupils went on <u>a</u> school trip.
   I bought <u>a</u> new mug, but then I dropped it on <u>the</u> floor.
   It's going to be <u>an</u> exciting day. We're going to <u>the</u> zoo.

2. There was **a** beautiful sunset.
   She is **an** experienced helicopter pilot.
   My friend has **an** identical twin.
   My dog is **the** best dog in **the** world.
   When I was walking near **the** River Avon, I saw **an** otter.

3. You should have underlined these words:
   I want to climb **that** mountain.
   A secret agent caught **those** criminals.
   The recipe says you need **some** sugar, eggs and flour.
   Your grandad is standing beside **that** car.

4. Susan climbed out of **her** window.
   Those birds are really loud.
   Have you ever been to **that** restaurant?
   Nazia is looking for **some** old photos.
   John really enjoyed reading **those** books about spaceships.
   This cake is the tastiest cake I've ever eaten.

Section 2 — Clauses and Phrases

Pages 17-19 — Clauses

1. The car <u>skidded</u> around the corner.
   Erin <u>did</u> her homework before school.
   Farmer Gregory <u>bought</u> some goats.
   The grumpy llama <u>chased</u> the hikers.
   The bats <u>flew</u> out of the cave.
   Mila the cat <u>ate</u> the whole fish.

2. You should have ticked these sentences:
   <u>Taio</u> dug a hole in the sand.
   <u>My neighbour</u> is an acrobat.
   <u>Nobody</u> knew what to say.
   <u>We</u> went to see the doctor.

3. <u>The monkey</u> watched the tourists. — subject
   My aunt Marta <u>made</u> the cake. — verb
   Jason and Mario <u>hummed</u> a tune. — verb
   <u>A swarm of bees</u> buzzed around us. — subject

4. Main clauses: we walked the dog, Graeme was sent home, the music was loud, he will come to visit us, the pigs snorted loudly
   Subordinate clauses: if he has time, as they ate the food, when the party started, after she hit Jo, before I had dinner

5. You should have ticked these sentences:
   The alarm beeped <u>until I turned it off</u>.
   You need to tell me <u>where you hid the toys</u>.
   I can have a puppy <u>provided that I take care of it</u>.

6. After he found the treasure, <u>the pirate stole it</u>.
   Before I go to bed, <u>I brush my teeth</u>.
   <u>Colette watered the flowers</u> because it was hot.
   <u>I climbed the tree</u> although I was scared.

7. You should have matched these pairs:
   I will wrap his presents — while he's at school.
   She cleaned her shoes — because they were muddy.
   I asked for hot drink — as it was cold outside.

8. Any suitable answer.
   Examples:
   Leo will come over **when he's finished his homework.**
   We can go to the cinema **if we are good.**
   Don't open your presents **until everyone is here.**

Pages 20-22 — Relative Clauses

1. She hid the book <u>that</u> I was looking for.
   Hamish is the child <u>who</u> lives next door.
   We went to the shop <u>which</u> sells fudge.
   We heard a musician <u>who</u> is very talented.
   I have a letter <u>which</u> is addressed to you.

2. You should have ticked these sentences:
   Mr Plump is the man who teaches history.
   We watched TV when we should have been asleep.
   Robbie was shocked when we surprised him.

3. Hazel swatted the fly <u>that was annoying her</u>.
   Nobody saw the children <u>who broke the window</u>.
   There's some food in the kitchen <u>which I saved for you</u>.
   Margot is the woman <u>whose dogs tried to bite me</u>.

4. Marco shouted at Billy, **who** was pulling silly faces.
   I looked for the football **which** we had lost.
   We bought a car **which** used to belong to a celebrity.
   Mum helped the old lady **who** had fallen over.

5. My cat has a kitten **whose** fur is black and white.
   Seth has lots of books **that** he has never read.
   I saw the mysterious man **who** thinks he's a wizard.

6. Are these the flowers **that** we planted last year?
   Here is the blanket **which** we took on the picnic.
   There's the man **who** I spoke to yesterday.
   Did you find the shoes **which** you were looking for?

7. He cleaned up the mess <u>he had made</u>.
   She chose the dress <u>she wanted</u>.
   Jim told me a story <u>I'd already heard</u>.

8. I think it's time I went home.

Page 23 — Phrases

1. You should have written 'P' next to these options:
   as quickly as possible, to the seaside,
   extremely annoying, before midnight, the old grey dog
   You should have written 'C' next to these options:
   they caught the chicken, the sea glinted,
   my parrot can talk

2. Phrases: near the supermarket, the colourful shell,
   a lemon lollipop, next to the chair
   Clauses: they speak Spanish, I used to play chess,
   the stars are shining, she borrowed a pen

Answers

Page 24 — Noun Phrases

1. Kate used three red and white **ribbons** to make the bows.
   The small, fluffy **lamb** was born yesterday.
   The chef used the shiniest red **tomatoes** for the sauce.
   Nathan cautiously sniffed the sticky **mixture**.
   The bright red **light** flickered in the darkness.

2. Any suitable answer.
   Examples:
   the **unlucky** giraffe with a knot in its neck
   the **giant** sailor on the tiny boat
   the **cheerful** penguin with the hat and gloves

Section 3 — Conjunctions and Prepositions

Page 25 — Co-ordinating Conjunctions

1. Georgie likes dogs, <u>but</u> she doesn't like frogs.
   I was sleepy, <u>for</u> it had been a busy day.
   Rahman was hungry, <u>so</u> he ate an apple.
   It was dark outside, <u>yet</u> Wiktoria wanted to go for a walk.
   We can play on the slide <u>or</u> we can play on the see-saw.
   He likes pink <u>and</u> he likes purple.

2. I'm going to the shops, **for** I need to buy some bananas.
   They are tired, **but** they don't want to go to sleep.
   I have hurt my leg, **so** I can't play outside.
   We can go home **or** we can go to see the palace.

Page 26 — Subordinating Conjunctions

1. We can play a game <u>while</u> we wait.
   <u>Although</u> it is not raining, he has brought an umbrella.
   You can stay for tea <u>unless</u> you want to go home.
   <u>Since</u> she caught a cold, she has been unable to talk.
   <u>After</u> you tidy up, you can play video games.
   I want to stay awake <u>until</u> I see a shooting star.

2. He eats sweets **even though** his tooth hurts.
   You can hold the snake **if** you want to.
   They are wet **because** they swam in the lake.

Page 27 — Using Conjunctions for Cohesion

1. Riya wants pizza for tea **but** Laura wants spaghetti.
   I don't like Zach **because** he broke my bicycle.
   He finished his homework **before** he went to play outside.
   At the fair, we went on the waltzers **and** we ate candyfloss.

2. We believe in aliens **because** we saw a spaceship.
   I bought you a present **but** I forgot it.
   She was cold **so** she put on a jumper.

Pages 28 and 29 — Prepositions

1. The boat is **next to** the island.
   The octopus is **in** the sea.
   The pirate is **on** the island.
   The treasure is **under** the tree.

2. Tanya, Halima and Max are meeting <u>at</u> the park.
   We eventually found the clue hidden <u>above</u> the door.
   I found some smelly socks <u>underneath</u> my bed.
   They will see the statue <u>before</u> going home.

She is travelling <u>from</u> her house.
He couldn't see because she was standing <u>in front of</u> the TV.

3. I have a piano lesson <u>until</u> 2.30 pm. — when
   They went home <u>after</u> the film. — when
   The park is <u>behind</u> the school. — where
   He has been dancing <u>since</u> this morning. — when
   My sister said we can go <u>to</u> the theme park. — where

4. We haven't seen her **since** last week.
   Before eating, they wash their hands.
   I had a painful headache **during** the show.
   He was playing **until** teatime.

5. Any suitable sentences.
   Examples:
   The dog is **under** the table.
   The table is **in front of** the window.
   The frog is **in** the tree.

Section 4 — Linking Ideas

Pages 30 and 31 — Linking Ideas in a Paragraph

1. Let's go for a walk <u>after lunch</u>.
   I can run <u>unbelievably fast</u>.
   He walks the dog <u>twice a day</u>.
   There's fruit <u>on the table</u>.
   <u>Every weekend</u> we got to town.
   She stroked the rabbit <u>very gently</u>.
   Kate cycled home <u>really slowly</u>.
   The class was quiet <u>this morning</u>.
   Ziyad is <u>in his room</u>.
   I found my sock <u>inside my shoe</u>.

2. You should have drawn lines to match these phrases:
   How — almost perfectly, extremely quickly, with a big smile, very quietly
   Where — in the garden, under the door mat, on the floor, near the bookshelf
   When — next week, much earlier, by tomorrow, last night

3. I like to go cycling **every weekend**.
   Her brother was playing music **so loudly**.
   There is a nice book shop **next to the bank**.
   We are going to bake cookies **this afternoon**.
   She thinks there is a monster **under the bed**.
   All of the cake had been eaten **by 12 o'clock**.

4. We are going on holiday **in three days**.
   On Saturday morning, I am going to visit my cousins.
   They are going to stay in a villa **next to** the beach.
   My sister Jannat can swim **really well**.
   After that, you will be hungry.
   We usually visit my grandparents **once a month**.
   He looked at me **with an angry scowl**.

Pages 32 and 33 — Linking Paragraphs

1. Place — on the roof, at the bus stop, in the kitchen, under the chair, behind the cushion
   Number — firstly, secondly, fourthly, thirdly
   Time — next month, in the morning, earlier, later that day, last year

2. Jasper the dog lay in the kitchen, snoozing in his basket as the sun came in through the window.
   In the garden, Alvin was cooking sausages on the

Answers

barbecue. They were almost ready to eat, and they sizzled as he turned them.

All of a sudden, he heard a shout from inside the house. Abandoning the barbecue, he ran inside to find out what was happening.

Inside, Suzie and Harmony were having an argument. They were shouting so loudly that they woke Jasper up from his nap.

With a big yawn, Jasper got up from his basket. His nose began to twitch as the delicious smell of sausages floated in from the garden.

3. There are lots of possible answers to this question. Make sure your answer includes two sentences, and that your first sentence starts with an adverbial phrase which you have underlined.
    Example:
    <u>After breakfast</u>, he said goodbye to his mum. She thought he was going to play with his friends, but Charlie had other ideas.

Section 5 — Verb Tenses

Page 34 — Present Tense and Past Tense

1. Past: Nora <u>went</u> out.
    Ty <u>finished</u> the pizza.
    Louise <u>gave</u> a speech.
    Present: Omar <u>makes</u> scones.
    Luke <u>studies</u> hard.
    Chelsea <u>does</u> karate.

2. This evening, I **cooked** chilli for my family.
    Ellen **played** the drums for the school band.
    The teacher said that you **worked** hard.
    Layton **ran** a long way today.
    We **did** all our homework on Saturday.

Pages 35 and 36 — Verbs with 'ing'

1. Maria **is** cooking.
    We **are** watching.
    They **are** playing.
    He **is** singing.
    The boys **are** talking.
    Ravi and I **are** eating.
    You **are** shouting.
    I **am** going.

2. Zoya **is building** a robot.
    We **are visiting** a theme park.
    Sid **is buying** a sausage roll.
    You **are looking** for your keys.
    I **am feeling** very sleepy now.

3. Past tense with 'ing': I was telling Noor.
    Troy was making toast.
    I was sitting there.
    They were feeling excited.
    Present tense with 'ing': Arjun is sleeping deeply.
    You are leaving today.
    Gabrielle is smiling.
    We are taking a break.

4. You should have completed the table like this:

Present tense with 'ing'	Past tense with 'ing'
Jade is calling Beth.	Jade was calling Beth.
Amir is going bowling.	Amir was going bowling.
They are having lunch.	**They were having lunch.**
We are starting a project.	**We were starting a project.**
You are reading a book.	You were reading a book.

5. Whiskers **was breaking** Granny's plates.
    We **were asking** for pudding.

Pages 37 and 38 — Past tense with 'have'

1. has: Sana **has** asked.
          Gethin **has** been.
          He **has** decided.
          The dog **has** barked.
    have: You **have** looked.
          We **have** built.
          They **have** washed.
          I **have** remembered.

2. Jack has **stayed** at home with Vanessa.
    Alice and Maisie have **raised** their hands.
    I have **waited** for this parcel for ages.
    We have **said** that we will go together.
    They have **made** a mess with their rubbish.
    Rosie has **bought** too much milk.

3. You should have completed the table like this:

Present tense	Past tense with 'have'
I reach	I **have reached**
he turns	he **has turned**
we want	we **have wanted**
you try	you **have tried**
they use	they **have used**

4. Ariana has **lost** her father's watch.
    Julian **has played** a tennis match today.
    I **have offered** to pay for the concert tickets.
    We have **grown** vegetables in the garden.
    I **have discovered** some hidden treasure.

5. Any suitable sentences that use the past tense with 'have'.
    Examples:
    I have played outside today.
    My mum has talked to my teacher.

Page 39 — Staying in the Same Tense

1. You should have matched these pairs:
    I jumped — you hopped
    I have asked — you have answered
    she eats — he drinks
    they are waiting — we are running

2. **writes** — The teacher goes to the board and **writes** the date.
    played — David met Harley in the park and they **played** for an hour.
    is making — Mum is chopping a carrot because she **is making** a stew.
    went — I played video games for a while before I **went** to bed.

Answers

3. Any suitable sentence that keeps both verbs in the same tense.
   Example:
   I **turn** the key and **open** the lock.

Section 6 — Standard and Non-Standard English

Pages 40-42 — Standard and Non-Standard English

1. Standard English: They have been out. She made a cake. You are funny. It was wonderful.
   Non-Standard English: Freddie like the biscuits. It were awful. I have did my best. We is making lunch.

2. **I** think the sweets look yummy.
   Grace pushed **me** over in the playground.
   Would you like to be friends with **me**?
   Ifran and **I** like playing wheelchair tennis.
   The teacher told **me** off for talking.

3. Please put **those** wrappers in the bin. — those
   Those two are playing on the beach. — those
   I will show **them** the canteen. — them
   He has finally found **them**. —them
   Who do **those** bags belong to? — those

4. You should have drawn lines to match the following sentences:
   I done it yesterday. — I did it yesterday.
   She has went home. — She has gone home.
   My mum give me £10. — My mum gave me £10.
   We was really hungry. — We were really hungry.

5. is
   goes
   are
   know
   want

6. I couldn't see **anybody**.
   They can't play outside **anymore**.
   He can't find the dog **anywhere**.
   Don't tell **anyone** about the surprise.

7. You should have ticked the following sentences:
   They don't like animals.
   They were nowhere to be seen.
   I can't hear anything.

8. Any relevant sentence written in Standard English.
   Example:
   He isn't talking to me.

Punctuation

Section 7 — Sentence Punctuation

Page 43 — Capital Letters and Full Stops

1. You should have ticked: martin, january, russia

2. **A**ndrea and **S**aul met for lunch in **M**anchester on **T**uesday. **T**hey talked about the **E**aster holidays. **S**aul had been to **P**ortugal with his friend, **E**mma, to see his favourite band.

3. **M**y cousin, **C**harlotte, owns her own business**.**
   In **E**dinburgh, **I** went to three museums**.**

Page 44 — Question Marks

1. <u>Which</u> pair of shoes do you prefer?
   <u>Whose</u> lunchbox has been left on the stairs?
   <u>How</u> can we explain this?
   <u>Where</u> should we go for lunch tomorrow?
   <u>Who</u> won the volleyball tournament?

2. Let's go to the cinema to see that new film**.**
   Would you like to go shopping with me this weekend**?**
   I enjoy exploring new places with my friends**.**
   Playing football is my favourite thing to do**.**
   How do you know the people you were talking to**?**
   Would you like lasagne for dinner tonight**?**

Page 45 — Exclamation Marks

1. You should have ticked:
   Put that down, now
   How dare you
   What a masterpiece
   Don't talk nonsense

2. Please make a shopping list**.**
   I was absolutely terrified**!**
   Come here immediately**!**
   You need to walk the dog**.**

3. Any suitable sentences.
   Examples:
   What a cheerful person!
   How annoying that song is!

Pages 46 and 47— Sentence Practice

1. Collect your bags from the classroom. — A command
   Thomas and Kara are my friends. — A statement
   Why do we have to get up so early? — A question
   What a big dog that is! — An exclamation

2. Have you ever built a sandcastle on the beach**?**
   How long and boring this journey is**!**
   Where would you like to go on holiday this year**?**
   Sandra has always enjoyed playing hockey**.**
   Give them their sandwiches back at once**!**

3. **T**wo years ago, **I** went skiing in **A**ustria with my family**. W**e were away for five days between **C**hristmas and **N**ew **Y**ear**. M**y brother learned to snowboard with an instructor called **K**elly**.**
   Miss **W**est is my **E**nglish teacher**. S**he always has a smile on her face**. S**he used to live in **N**ew **Z**ealand, but now she lives in **K**ent**. S**he's bringing her rabbit, called **H**oppy, to school on **F**riday**.**

4. Any suitable sentences.
   Examples:
   What a powerful wizard that is!
   What is the boy reading?
   Margaret was late for her meeting.

Section 8 — Commas

Pages 48 and 49 — Commas in Lists

1. **Jacob** used commas correctly.

2. You should have put commas in these places:
   The weather tomorrow will be cloudy**,** windy and rainy.
   I will be able to visit on Friday**,** Saturday or Sunday.

Answers

Would you like apple, orange or blackcurrant juice?
We will see Martha, Levi and Rhys at the after school club.
Shall we go to France, Spain or Italy on holiday this year?

3. You should have added these commas:
I like toffees, fudge, caramels and peppermints.
Hamsters, rabbits, gerbils and guinea pigs are all good pets.
The bracelet was covered in emeralds, rubies and diamonds.
Mars, Jupiter and Venus are all planets near to Earth.
My friends' birthdays are in January, March and June.
I took part in the long jump, hurdles, sprint and relay.

4. To keep fit, I **walk to school, ride my bike, do karate and play fetch with my dog.**
Before the school play, I need to **learn my lines, make my costume, practise my song and sell some tickets.**

Pages 50 and 51 — Commas to Join Sentences

1. You should have ticked these sentences:
We are tired, yet we want to stay awake until midnight.
I am going to the supermarket, for I have run out of milk.
I can watch television, or I can play video games.

2. You should have added commas to these sentences:
I like puzzles, so I do one every night.
I must go now, or I will be late again.

3. Kirsty played netball, **and** she scored seven goals.
We could cook dinner, **or** we could order takeaway.
The forecast predicted rain, **so** Elijah wore his coat.
Jasmine waited for the bus, **but** the bus did not come.

4. You should have added commas in these places:
Jake did not bring a pen today, nor did he bring a pencil.
I want to read a new book, for I have read the book I have.
We are hungry, yet we cannot eat anything until lunchtime.
There was a great sale, so I bought twenty pairs of socks!

5. Zia planted seeds, **and** they grew quickly.
We guessed the answer, **but** it was wrong.
The view was great, **so** I took a photo.

Pages 52 and 53 — Commas After Introductions

1. You should have ticked these sentences:
In ten years, I want to be a successful Olympic gymnast.
An hour ago, the postman brought a parcel for me.
Once a week, I have to babysit my cousin Alannah.

2. **In prehistoric times,** humans made useful tools out of rocks.
In silence, the class work hard at their reading test.
In France, Lea tried croissants and jam for breakfast.
At weekends, Spenser helps his dad wash the car.

3. You should have added commas in these places:
With great care, I checked whether any cars were approaching.
As slowly as possible, Jason walked towards the door.
During Queen Victoria's reign, women usually wore dresses.
In Edinburgh, I saw a huge, old castle on a hill.
The day after tomorrow, Ali is going to play badminton with me.
Every morning, Brook eats breakfast and then brushes her teeth.

4. **Under the sofa, I found an old letter.**
Every day, Sophia walks her dog.

5. Any suitable sentence that includes a comma after the adverbial phrase.
Example:
After the show, **the pianist received a huge round of applause.**

Pages 54 and 55 — Commas for Extra Information

1. You should have ticked these sentences:
The baker, Mr Miller, saved me my favourite sandwich.
I visited Natalia, a childhood friend, when I went to Devon.
My village, which is tiny, has hardly any shops.

2. You should have drawn lines to create these sentences:
The firefighters, Kit and Cara, came to help.
We have sausages, my favourite food, on Saturdays.
Umar cycles uphill, which is difficult, to get to school.

3. You should have added commas in these places:
The pupils, whose names were Erica and Scott, got detentions.
Harley, the youngest player, was allowed the first turn.
Ben learnt about Egypt, where the pyramids are, in History.
Amara's two rabbits, Primrose and Bluebell, are very cute.
Dinner, which is spaghetti and meatballs, is at 6 o'clock.
The concert, which I am really excited about, is on Friday.

4. You should have put the extra information in these places:
My teacher, **whose name is Miss Brooks,** know lots about maths.
The new cinema, **which is on the main road,** has just opened.
The Eiffel Tower, **which is a famous landmark,** is in Paris.

Pages 56 and 57 — Comma Practice

1. You should have ticked these sentences:
In summer, I like to go swimming in the ocean.
I go to the restaurant, and I order a steak.
You should have crossed these sentences:
My favourite colours are purple blue, and orange.
My friends Nia and Li are having a joint birthday party.
In the future cars might be able to drive themselves.

2. Today I need to **tidy my room, do my homework, feed my pet snake and ring Grandad.**

3. **At low tide,** Tamika went looking for starfish.
Kevin, **who was very light,** was good at the pole vault.
The Angel of the North, **a famous statue,** is in Gateshead.
With great care, Hassan completed the science experiment.
In autumn, I love watching the leaves change colour.
My uncles, **Richard and Michael,** have two children.

4. You should have made these sentences:
The sun is bright, **so** I put on suncream.
I went shopping, **and** I bought new boots.
I ask for directions, **for** I have no map.

Section 9 — Brackets and Dashes

Pages 58 and 59 — Brackets for Extra Information

1. You should have ticked these sentences:
Our headteacher (Mr Bruce) cycles to school.
I bought some pears (my favourite fruit) and plums.
The plane (the biggest one I've ever seen) is taking off.

2. My little brother (a keen artist) spilt some paint.
I added chillies to the meal (a spicy curry).

Answers

He and his friend (who met last year) play football together.
Jermaine studied two subjects (English and French) at university.
Maximillian (Max to his friends) was a successful businessman.

3. Karl and Marie (the bank robbers) couldn't crack the safe.
I overtook the vehicle (a caravan) on the motorway.
Joan played the lead role (a powerful superhero) in the film.
Darcey beat her previous record (4 goals) during the match.

4. Any suitable phrases.
Examples:
Carrie's doll (**her favourite one**) is quite old.
The tickets (**the ones for the rock concert**) were expensive.
The caretaker (**an old man**) repaired the door.

5. The cow (the brown one) is eating grass.
She bought a drink (a coffee) at the café.

Pages 60 and 61 — Dashes for Extra Information

1. **Devlin** used dashes correctly.

2. You should have crossed out the dashes in brackets and added the dashes in bold.
I went for a walk — a (—) long one — in the woods.
We read (—) Macbeth — a play by Shakespeare — in class.
Somebody — for the (—) second time — had taken my mug.

3. Oona — a gymnast — is training for a competition.
Mike pours a drink — a glass of water — from the jug.
Lions and wolves — both excellent hunters — live in groups.
Dylan kicked the football — a new one — into the stream.

4. You should have put a cross next to this sentence:
My dad built — with a bit of help a — treehouse last summer.
Corrected sentence:
My dad built — with a bit of help — a treehouse last summer.

5. Tasty meals — especially stews — take a while to cook.

6. The family — two parents and six children — are friendly.
The rocket — the red one with the yellow stripes — is flying into space.
We're going on holiday — two weeks in Italy — in July.

Section 10 — Apostrophes

Page 62 — Apostrophes for Missing Letters

1. I will — **I'll**, we have — **we've**, he would — **he'd**,
they had — **they'd**, can not — **can't**, who is — **who's**

2.

is not	isn't		let us	let's
do not	don't		has not	hasn't
I have	I've		should not	shouldn't

3. **They'll** go if he **hasn't** lost the tickets.

Page 63 — Its and It's

1. belonging to — Its feet are huge.
it is — It's green and fluffy.
it has — It's been changed.

2. You should have ticked these sentences:
It's ready to go.
It's a very tough job.
They fixed its problems.

3. You should have added these apostrophes:
The baby has an apple in its hand — it's adorable!
It's been a lovely day — it's perfect weather for a BBQ.
It's important to look after your bag or its straps could break.

Pages 64 and 65 — Apostrophes for Single Possession

1. The waiter's jacket was pink.
A bee's sting is painful.
The woman's dinner was tasty.
The walrus's tusks are long.

2. mum's, donkey's, coat's, flamingo's

3. You should have ticked these sentences:
the zebra's stripes
the cheese's smell
the glass's design

4. The **shirt's** button has fallen off.
My **sister's** room is next to mine.
Our **class's** behaviour is good.
Gloria's shoes are orange and purple.

5. That's **Mario's** bike.
Those are **Jess's** books.
That is **my cousin's** doll.
Those are **Elvis's** sunglasses.
That is **Sven's** ball.

Pages 66 and 67 — Apostrophes for Plural Possession

1. **bats'**, **geese's**, **women's**, **elves'**, **desks'**, **nails'**

2. We threw a surprise party for my **sisters'** birthdays.
The light can be seen from the **houses'** windows.
The **curtains'** patterns are quite old-fashioned.
Mice's tails are usually shorter than rats' tails.

3. the monkeys' hands
the men's shoes
the teachers' meeting
the people's voices
the dogs' dinners

4. You should have ticked these sentences:
The polar bears' home is in the Arctic.
The children's faces lit up when they saw her.
The horses' hooves are sore from running all day.
None of the shirts' buttons are sewn on properly.
Sharks' teeth are extremely sharp.
You should have crossed these sentences:
This bookshop sells the best authors's books.
The cakes's decorations look really pretty.
Corrected sentences:
The bookshop sells the best **authors'** books.
The **cakes'** decorations look really pretty.

Pages 68 and 69 — Apostrophe Practice

1. You should have ticked these sentences:
Jamie's dog hasn't ever barked at anyone.
I should walk to the shops but it's going to rain.
Matt is going out but he's forgotten his wallet.

Answers

2. that is — **that's**, you would — **you'd**,
   they are — **they're**, does not — **doesn't**,
   she will — **she'll**, he had — **he'd**, was not — **wasn't**,
   will not — **won't**

3. the boy's friends — one boy has more than one friend
   the boys' friends — two boys have more than
   one friend
   the boy's friend — one boy has one friend
   the boys' friend — two boys have one friend

4. Shelley gave the cat **its** food.
   The guide dog led **its** owner.
   I can't use my car — **it's** broken.
   The trampoline has lost **its** bounce.
   It's time for your piano lesson.
   The squirrel buried **its** nuts.
   It's not a joke — this is serious.

5. the biker's helmet
   the giraffe's neck
   the carpenters' tools
   the waitresses' notepads
   the lizards' tongues

Section 11 — Inverted Commas

Pages 70 and 71 — Punctuating Speech

1. "Please tidy your room before dinner," said Mum.
   The judge announced, "The winner is Nadia."
   "I swept up the leaves," she said.
   Ibrahim explained, "I didn't eat your sandwich."
   "He told me what you did," said the teacher**.**

2. **"**Can I look after your dog?**"** asked my friend.
   "We should work together on the project,**"** said Polly.
   Mr Lipton shouted, **"**Get out of my garden!**"**
   The police officer asked, **"**What did the thief look like?**"**

3. You should have ticked these sentences:
   She said, "Give the red sweets to Larry."
   "I need to visit the dentist soon," said Shona.

4. Sophie said, "Netball is my favourite sport**.**"
   "What time does it start**?**" asked Liam**.**
   "How exhausted I am**!**" he exclaimed**.**
   "You should eat more fruit,**"** said the doctor**.**

5. **"**I will help you build a sandcastle," said Mia.
   "Take the dog for a walk,**"** said Dad**.**
   "Can we plant some flowers**?**" asked my little brother.
   Johan shouted**,** "Show me where you've hidden the toys!**"**

Pages 72 and 73 — Direct and Reported Speech

1. Direct speech:
   "I can't tell you because it's a secret," he said.
   "Listen to me!" yelled Kyle.
   Benaiah asked, "What is that smell?"
   Reported speech:
   Lynn said you should ask him.
   They told us you went to London.

2. You should have matched the following pairs:
   "I'm very thirsty," said Kirsty. — Kirsty said she was thirsty.
   We said, "We can't go today." — We said we couldn't go today.
   Zack shouted, "Come back!" — Zack shouted for us to come back.

3. You should have ticked these sentences:
   I can't find my gloves, said Ameera.
   Vinny said, This level is easier than the first one.
   My name is Feathers, said the parrot.

4. Direct speech:
   "Why are you upset?"
   "Get out of my way!"
   "Let's buy them a gift."
   Reported speech:
   He said he hates cats.
   We told them to behave.
   I said I needed help.

Section 12 — Paragraphs and Layout

Pages 74 and 75 — Paragraphs

1. You should have ticked these sentences:
   You want to write about a new place.
   Someone new is going to speak.
   You want to write about a different topic.
   You want to write about a different time.

2. You should have matched these sentences:
   Sailing is a fun and relaxing hobby for people who like the sea. — You can compete in races or sail to distant places.
   Halim likes to watch sport on the television. — He loves football because he enjoys the commentary.
   The weather has been unusually warm this summer. — Yesterday broke the record for the hottest day of the year.

3. You should have added these paragraph markers:
   Today, my class worked outside because the weather was so nice. We drew pictures of the flowers in the school field. I drew a daffodil. // When we were done, Mr Davies told us to go to the pond. // "How exciting!" said my friend Martha, "I've never been there before." // At the pond, we looked for frogs and newts.
   Correct reasons:
   2nd paragraph: new time
   3rd paragraph: new person speaking
   4th paragraph: new place

4. Any suitable sentences that could go in the same paragraph.
   Examples:
   Holiday resorts offer a range of activities. **You can swim in the pool or play games in the arcade.**
   My brother is called Josh. **He is two years younger than me and has blue eyes.**
   The library has all sorts of books. **The children's section has both fiction and non-fiction books.**

Page 76 — Headings and Subheadings

1. CLARA'S CAKE COMPANY — heading
   All sizes, shapes and flavours — subheading
   Free delivery — subheading
   Contact us! — subheading

2. You should have matched these pairs:
   September — School starts now, so all our pupils will be excited to meet their new teachers...
   October — Have a spooky costume ready, as Halloween is just around the corner...
   December — It's almost time for the Christmas holidays and the Nativity play is ready to go...

Answers

Spelling

Section 13 — Prefixes

Page 77 — Prefixes — 're' 'anti' and 'auto'

1. **react, rewrite, recount, anticlockwise, antibacterial**

2. The actress has just written an **auto**biography about her life.
   The ghost **re**appeared on the other side of the wall.
   When I fell over, my mum put **anti**septic cream on my grazes.
   Marc asked for the tennis player's **auto**graph after the game.

Pages 78 and 79 — Prefixes — 'under' 'over' 'en' and 'em'

1. Mike worried that he was <u>under</u>performing at school.
   The train was <u>over</u>crowded and really noisy.
   The garden of the abandoned house was really <u>over</u>grown.

2. You should have ticked:
   My brother won't <u>over</u>eat because he hates feeling too full.
   Jamal baked his cake for too long so it was <u>over</u>cooked.

3. **underpaid, overload, underrated**

4. I want to **en**large this photograph to hang on the wall.
   Luci tried to be quiet so she didn't **en**rage the teacher.
   Niall couldn't escape the **em**brace of Great Aunt Maggie.
   I'd like to set a good example and **en**courage others.
   The couple are about to **em**bark on a journey together.

5. **enclose, enchant, empower**
   A wicked wizard tried to **enchant** the princess.
   I hope the speech will **empower** people.
   They are planning to **enclose** the field with a fence.

Pages 80 and 81 — Prefixes — 'mid' 'pre' 'fore' and 'non'

1. **forefinger, nonprofit, foreground, nonverbal, nonstick**

2. The weather is really hot in **midsummer**.
   We had to **preselect** what we wanted for lunch.
   She is the best **midfielder** in the team.
   We're learning about **prehistoric** creatures in class.
   After 3 days, I reached the **midpoint** of my 6-day holiday.

3. Words beginning 'mid-': **midair, midnight**
   Words beginning 'pre-': **prearrange, prepay**
   Words beginning 'fore-': **foresee, forehead**
   Words beginning 'non-': **nonstop, nonsense**

4. **forewarn, preview**

5. The baby was born early — it was **premature**.
   Every day, I have a **midmorning** cup of tea.

Section 14 — Word Endings and Suffixes

Pages 82 and 83 — Word Endings — the 'shun' sound

1. e**lectrician**, m**usician**, p**olitician**, **optician**

2. **action, fiction, mention, invitation, mathematician, conversation, position, technician, hesitation**

3. I watched the colourful carnival **procession** go past.
   After school, we watched cartoons on the **television**.
   When the volcano erupted, there was a huge **explosion**.
   My parents gave me **permission** to go on the school trip.
   Elliot and I had never heard that **version** of the song.

4. tion:
   relate — **relation**
   sion:
   collide — **collision**
   extend — **extension**
   confuse — **confusion**
   ssion:
   discuss — **discussion**
   admit — **admission**

Pages 84 and 85 — Word Endings — 'ant' and 'ent'

1. Words ending 'ant': expect**ant**, reluct**ant**, contest**ant**
   Words ending 'ent': independ**ent**, abs**ent**, incid**ent**, intellig**ent**, instrum**ent**

2. import**ent** — **important**
   pati**ant** — **patient**
   urg**ant** — **urgent**
   brilli**ent** — **brilliant**

3. **present, silent, distant, ancient, servant**

4. The teacher wrote on the board in **permanent** marker.
   Kian told some really funny jokes in his **recent** show.
   France is part of the European **continent**.
   Thea thought the summer picnic was very **pleasant**.
   The magician's stage name was Marco the **Magnificent**.
   It is **convenient** to have a shop around the corner.

5. The **disobedient elephant** escaped from the zoo.

Pages 86 and 87 — Word Endings — 'ance', 'ancy' and 'ence', 'ency'

1. Correct spelling:
   instance
   absence
   obedience
   balance
   Incorrect spelling:
   sciance
   patiance
   ignorence
   innocance

2. evid**ence**, inf**ancy**, nuis**ance**, urg**ency**, pres**ence**, adv**ance**

3. The band gave an incredible **performance**.
   People who act with **decency** make good friends.
   Henry called an ambulance because it was an **emergency**.
   I don't have much **experience** of looking after pets.
   A **pregnancy** usually lasts about nine months.

4. 1 — aud**ience**
   2 — guid**ance**
   3 — curr**ency**
   4 — confid**ence**
   5 — vac**ancy**
   6 — **ent**r**ance**

Answers

Pages 88 and 89 — Word Endings — 'able', 'ible', 'ably' and 'ibly'

1. Words ending 'able': avail**able**, adapt**able**, like**able**, love**able**
   Words ending 'ible': terr**ible**, flex**ible**, respons**ible** imposs**ible**

2. reason — **reasonable**, **reasonably**
   a**ccess** — **accessible**, **accessibly**

3. excit**ably**, invis**ibly**, sens**ibly**, fashion**ably**, respect**ably**, poss**ibly**

4. My parents' new sofa was very **comfortable**.
   I found a **suitable** dress for the party in the sale.
   The weather is absolutely **horrible** today.
   Simone took a **sizeable** piece of chocolate cake.
   He said he could cook, but his food was barely **edible**.

5. The schoolchildren were impecc**ably** dressed in their uniforms.
   Niamh's mum was justifi**ably** angry that she hadn't tidied up.
   Martyn was incred**ibly** upset after hearing the news.
   A thick layer of snow is vis**ibly** settling on the ground.
   Our class did remark**ably** well in sports day this year.

Pages 90 and 91 — Suffixes

1. weird**ly**, fam**ous**, timid**ly**, enorm**ous**, vari**ous**, bare**ly**, gorge**ous**, love**ly**, hazard**ous**, right**ly**, live**ly**, humor**ous**

2. -ify: class, solid, just, test
   -ise: real, final, familiar, organ, custom, advert

3. During the holidays, we are going to **decorate** my bedroom.
   Arlo must **specify** which route he wants us to take.
   Spenser and Seren are going to **revise** for the spelling test.
   I can't hear my phone **vibrate** when it's in my pocket.
   The hotel can **accommodate** up to 70 people.
   I will **summarise** the plot of the book for you.

4. happy — **happily**
   scary — **scarily**
   day — **daily**

5. danger**ous**, origin**ate**, joy**ous**, moment**ous**, passion**ate**

Section 15 — Confusing Words

Pages 92 and 93 — 'ei' and 'ie' Words

1. w**ei**ght, sc**ie**ntist, p**ie**ce, ch**ie**f
   You should have linked the words to these pictures:

chief

piece

weight

scientist

2. Marie was determined to ach**ie**ve all her goals.
   She felt a huge sense of rel**ie**f when her test was over.
   Jack couldn't bel**ie**ve what he had seen.
   Sophie likes to go on holiday to for**ei**gn countries.
   I flipped my pancake too high and it stuck to the c**ei**ling.

3. **seize**, **species**, **protein**, **friend**
   Protein is an important part of a balanced diet.
   Annika is going on holiday with her best **friend**.
   The police are going to **seize** the criminal's stolen goods.
   They have discovered a new **species** of shark.

4. Across: 1. mischief
           2. field
           3. thief
   Down: 1. ancient
         2. receipt
         3. weird

Pages 94 and 95 — Words with 'ough' in

1. **Hani** pronounces the 'ough' sound correctly.

2. **tough**, **roughly**, **doughnut**, **cough**, **trough**

3. Words with an 'or' sound: **thought**, **sought**, **ought**, **thoughtful**
   Words with an 'ow' sound: **drought**, **bough**

4. **plough** and **bough**
   thorough and **borough**
   bought and **nought**

5. **brought**, **thought**, **drought**, **through**

Pages 96 and 97 — Words with Silent Letters

1. **k**nickers, **w**reck, thum**b**, ans**w**er, dum**b**, **h**onest

2. **knee**, **lamb**, **wrist**, **ghost**

3. castle, plumber, knuckle, sword

4. Silent b words: **doubt**, **tomb**
   Silent w words: **wristband**, **wrinkle**, **shipwreck**, **wrath**
   Silent k words: **knobbly**, **doorknob**, **knot**

5. **biscuits**, **knight**, **scissors**

6. **wrestle**, **climb**, **whistle**
   Maya is going to **climb** Mount Everest this summer.
   The referee blew his **whistle** at the end of the game.
   My sisters used to **wrestle** each other in the hall.

Pages 98 and 99 — Homophones

1. **witch**, **which**, **write**, **right**

2. weak — **week**, bawl — **ball**, new — **knew**, meddle — **medal**, grate — **great**, flower — **flour**

3. bare — uncovered
   bear — a furry animal
   pair — two of something
   pear — a fruit
   flee — to run away
   flea — a small insect

4. The wind was so strong that it **blew** the roof off my house.
   "There's someone I'd like you to **meet**," said Toby.
   Millie had to **wait** two hours for her appointment.
   Every morning, I put blueberries on my **cereal**.

5. Mhairi **rode** her bike down the **road**.
   We were **bored** so we played a **board** game.
   Marcus saw a boat's **sail** for **sale**.

EG5FW21